STARTING

CDT

KEITH GOOD

Heinemann CDT in Action

Heinemann Educational Books

Heinemann Educational Books Ltd
22 Bedford Square, London WC1B 3HH

London Edinburgh Melbourne Auckland
Singapore Kuala Lumpur New Delhi
Ibadan Nairobi Johannesburg
Portsmouth (NH) Kingston

ISBN 0 435 75400 9

The publishers wish to thank the
following for kind permission to include
photographs:

Canon (p.37); Lego UK Ltd (p.108);
J. Allan Cash (Fig.1, p.119); all other
photos by the author

Front cover 'desk tidy' designed by
David Sarton, Angley School,
Cranbrook, Kent.

Designed by KAG Design Limited,
Basingstoke, Hampshire
Typeset by Kempshott Phototypesetting
Services, Basingstoke, Hampshire
Printed in Great Britain by
Scotprint Ltd., Musselburgh

To the reader

I hope this book will help you to enjoy CDT and to design and make some good projects. Even if you have never done this subject before, this book will give you lots of ideas. Here's what you'll find in the different chapters — the symbols will help you find your way around the book.

1 Designing your project

These pages tell you about CDT and show you how important designing is. You will also find ideas to help you tackle *any* design project. See how John and Sarah use these ideas when designing something for their local playgroup.

2 Working out your ideas and explaining them to others

Use these pages to find out what to use and how to draw and model your ideas. With help from this chapter you can produce a clear and attractive design folder even if you usually find drawing difficult.

3 Choosing the right materials for your project

Like all designers, you will need to know about materials and which is best for a particular job. These pages help you choose and give ideas for using materials wisely, avoiding waste and saving money.

4 Cutting and shaping parts for your project

These pages show you which tools to use and how to work safely with different materials. As usual in CDT, ask your teacher if you aren't sure about anything.

5 Joining parts of your project together

Lots of projects are made from more than one piece. These pages help you to choose the best joining method and show you how to join parts step-by-step.

6 Making your projects work: movement and control

Here you'll find all sorts of ways to bring your projects to life, including making things move, controlling them and using electronic parts. Use it to give you ideas when you are designing and to help get things working when making your project.

You can use *all* these chapters when designing your project and planning practical work. Use it when you are making your project too, if you want to find out how to do something or remind you of things your teacher has shown you.

Starting CDT: Projects

The projects which accompany this book include page references which will help you to find the right place in the book for ideas and information.

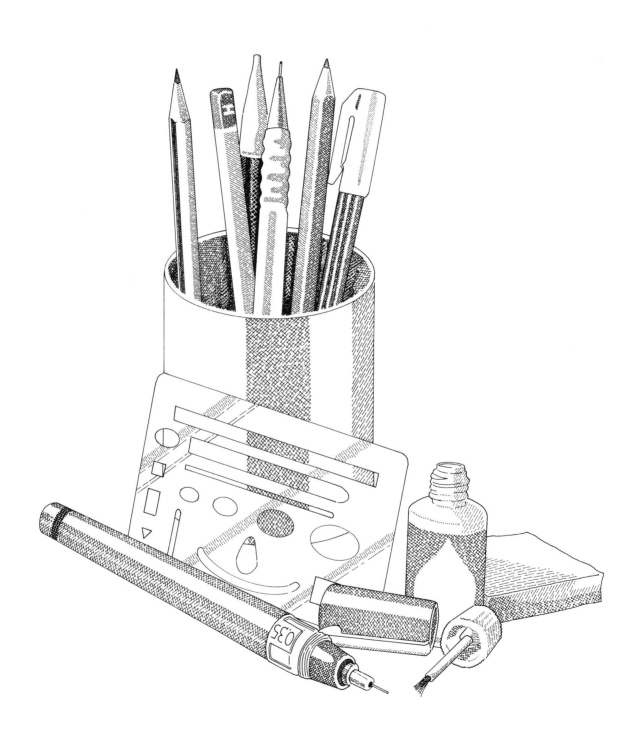

Contents

How do I design my project?

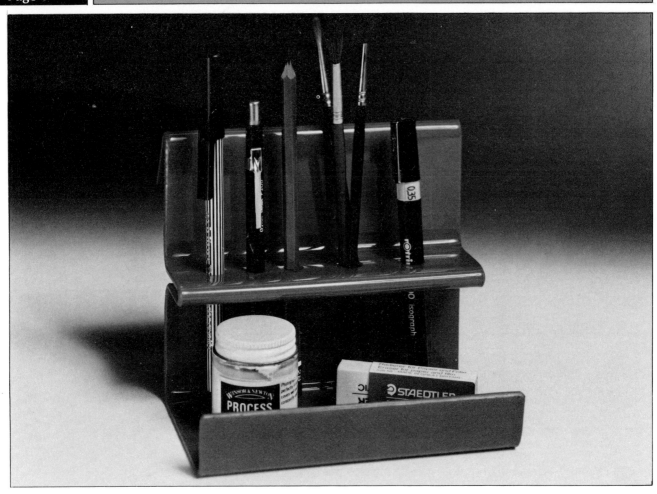

This desk tidy was designed and made by David Sarton of Angley School, Cranbrook, Kent. It is made from single sheet acrylic, and can be free-standing or hang neatly on the edge of a drawing board.

What will you do in CDT?

Craft, Design and Technology (CDT) may sound like a new subject but you have probably been doing CDT activities for a long time because they are fun. The children in Fig. 1 are working out ways of using materials to make something they want, finding ways round difficulties as they go along. This is a simple form of CDT.

Now you are older, deciding how to make things and trying to make them better can be even more interesting and exciting. You can work with real tools and materials which will last. Some of your projects will make life better for people, which is also part of CDT.

Fig. 1 You have probably used materials to solve problems already.

Fig. 2 These are some of the activities you can enjoy in CDT.

CDT includes lots of different activities which help to make it enjoyable. Look at Fig. 2 and glance through the rest of the book to get an idea of the variety of things you can do in this subject.

Say how you think your future projects will be different from things you could have designed and made when you were much younger.

Why is CDT so important?

CDT is about designing and making objects that will solve problems and make things better. This has always been important to people (Fig. 1) and probably always will be. Our health, wealth, comfort and safety depend on how well things are designed and made. You can probably think of some examples.

People have always designed and made things for all sorts of reasons. But *changes* have never happened so fast before. You probably use some of the things in Fig. 2 and they affect the way you live. Yet many of them did not exist just a short time ago. Can you think of other examples?

CDT teaches you ways of coping with problems you haven't met before. This is a good way of preparing you for a future full of changes and new ideas.

▌You are a consumer

As Fig. 2 shows, you are already a **consumer** or user of lots of things that have been designed and made. Working out how things *should* be designed and made is part of CDT and will help you to judge the things you might buy.

1 *Make a list of things that you remember seeing in the shops for the first time.*
2 *Make a list of things that your parents, teacher or a much older person remembers appearing in shops for the first time.*
You could start by asking them about things in Fig. 2.

Fig. 1 Designing and making to solve problems has always been important to people.

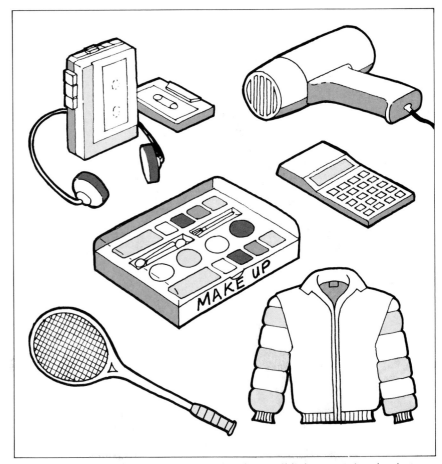

Fig. 2 **You are a consumer:** designing and making will help you judge the design and quality of manufactured things you might buy.

What is good design and why does it matter?

Designers don't always get things right. A badly designed and made project can make life difficult for people, or even harm them. It can also look ugly. Good projects work well *and* look good.

Whether something looks good or not depends on what you like. Although there are some things that most people would agree are ugly or attractive, a thing can look good in one setting and bad in another. This is sometimes called **aesthetics.**

Industrial design

Industrial designers try to make sure that *lots* of people think their products are attractive. Your designs should look good too, although you may not have to please everybody.

Products need to look good before people will buy them. The product in Fig. 1 needs to work well in the ways shown, and perhaps in other ways you can think of.

Poor design

As a buyer and user of products you need to decide if they look good and will work well. As a designer and maker you have to make the same decisions.
In Fig. 2 they got it badly wrong!

> 1 Look at Fig. 2 and say what is wrong with the way this ride-on toy was designed and made.
> 2 List the things you would look for if buying a ride-on toy for a young child. Use drawings to help you explain.

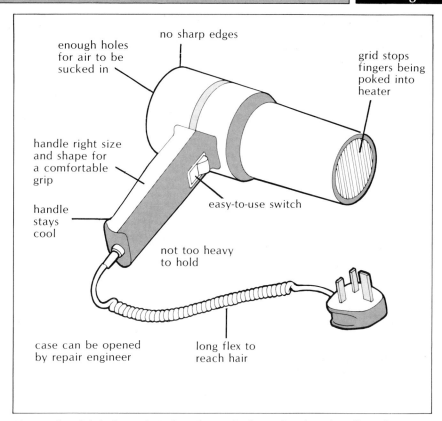

Fig. 1 **Industrial design:** a hair-dryer has to look good *and* work well; so do most other things that we buy or design.

Fig. 2 **Poor design:** when something is badly designed and made, people suffer.

Problems, problems, decisions, decisions!

In old-style woodwork and metalwork lessons, pupils practised using tools by copying the teacher's idea (Fig. 1).
In CDT you are given problems to solve instead of something to copy. Using tools is only part of this; you need to *ask questions* and *make decisions* too.

▌Find out more about the problem

How can you make sure that your projects are well designed? Well you should start by finding out more about the problem you have been given. A design problem that looks simple often has lots of interesting parts when you start to think about it (Fig. 2). You need to work out what parts your particular problem has and make sure your design takes care of them.
As Fig. 2 shows, you can end up with rather a lot of things to decide, even on an easy-looking problem.

▌A Master Plan!

You might think that the people in Fig. 2 have a right to look a bit baffled. *Don't panic!* On the next page you will find a **Master Plan** that will help with all your design problems and make them seem less frightening!

Choose a product that you would like to buy or design and make. This could be real, or imaginary like a time machine. Make a list of the different things you would need to think about when choosing or designing your product. Fig. 2 might get you started but each product will have its own list of problems to solve.

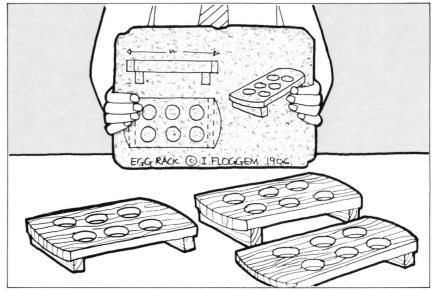

Fig. 1 CDT is *not* just another name for woodwork!

Fig. 2 **Find out more about the problem:** a design problem that sounds simple may have lots of interesting parts. The 'Master Plan' and other parts of this book will help you.

A Master Plan to help with your design problems

Here is a basic plan that can be used to help you tackle all kinds of design problems. It is often called the **design process**. The rest of this chapter tells you more about it.

The order shown below (**1 – 5**) is an easy one to follow. Sometimes you might have to go back to an earlier stage before you can go on. For example, you might find when making your project (**4**) that something doesn't work as you thought. You may go back to an earlier stage for a way round the problem.

1 **Setting out the problem — *The Design Brief***
If your teacher sets the problem, everyone in the class will start from the same place, but you will each be able to follow your own ideas and adapt the project to your own needs. As you become more experienced you may be asked to find problems for yourself. Page 7 tells you more.

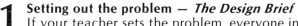

2 **Asking questions about the problem — *Investigation and Research***
Asking questions helps you to work out what is really needed and what key points you are to bear in mind. Gathering information — **research** — helps to give you ideas. There are lots of ways to do this (see pages 8, 9 and 10).

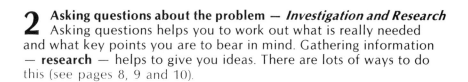

3 **Finding ideas and choosing the best one — *Solutions***
The best design is often made up parts of two or more ideas put together. Before you start making it the details have to be worked out. Making models and drawings helps you to sort out ideas and demonstrate them to your teacher (see chapter 2). This helps to prevent expensive mistakes.

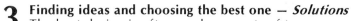

4 **Making the project you have designed — *Realisation***
A well-designed project can fail if it is badly made. Be as neat and accurate as you can. Your teacher's demonstrations and advice, and help from this book, should see you through your project safely.

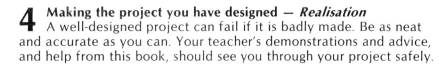

5 **How well does your project solve the problem? — *Testing and Evaluation***
Check back to the design brief you started with. You may need to work through some of the stages again to make improvements. After trying your project, try to think of ways to make it even better. Would you change anything if you were starting again?

▌ Keep a design folder
Use a design folder to record the different stages of your project and keep it together in order. It shows your thinking and is an important part of the finished product.

Setting out the problem — the design brief

CDT involves trying to solve a wide variety of practical problems. It is important to understand exactly what your problem is right from the start. Figure 1 shows a **design brief** given to two pupils, John and Sarah. You will be following their progress in this chapter.

▌ The design brief

A design brief helps by telling you clearly what is needed. Keep checking back to the brief to make sure you are doing what it asks.

▌ Design limits

When you start designing your teacher will probably set briefs that give you lots of information and hints about what to do. Certain materials, and ways of shaping and joining them, may be part of the brief (Fig. 2). These **design limits** put you on the right track and make sure that you learn important skills and methods that you will need later on.

When you are more experienced your teacher will give you fewer instructions and encourage you to make more decisions for yourself. This will include finding problems for yourself and writing your own design briefs.

John and Sarah now have to work out some important questions about their project. Write down what you think they need to think about.

Fig. 1 **The design brief:** John and Sarah were given a problem to solve.

Fig 2 **Design limits:** the brief included limits on materials and time. Like all designers, John and Sarah had to bear these in mind.

Investigating the problem — questions, questions!

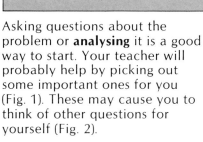

Asking questions about the problem or **analysing** it is a good way to start. Your teacher will probably help by picking out some important ones for you (Fig. 1). These may cause you to think of other questions for yourself (Fig. 2).

The questions you need to ask will depend on your particular problem, but here are some general ones that will help with most projects. Some of these may already be answered by the limits of your brief.

1 How long have I got to design and make this project?
When time is short it will affect which of the ideas you choose.

2 What materials will I be given and what others can I get?
Your teacher may say what and how much material you can use. Chapter 3 will help. Don't forget all the free parts and materials you can collect (see pages 56, 57 and 58).

3 What size and shape will make it easy and comfortable to use?
This is sometimes called **ergonomics,** a good word to impress people with!

4 How should it look?
This includes making it fit in with its surroundings. Think about colour, material and shape.

5 How will I put it together and make it work?
Chapters 4, 5 and 6 will help you to work out the order for tackling practical jobs.

6 How can I make it safe to use?
Last but *not* least — make sure that your design will help people, not harm them.

Fig. 1 John and Sarah's teacher picked out a key question to help them.

Fig. 2 Sarah thought of another key question. Safety was especially important on this project.

Fig. 3 John and Sarah wrote down and sketched the key questions in their design folders.

Imagine you have to work on the following two projects. Make a list of the questions you would want to ask about each problem.
(a) A unit to store video tapes.
(b) A lighting unit

Getting ideas and information — research

This book is one place to look for information to give you ideas. Remember, you are trying to come up with *your* answer to the problem, not to copy someone else's.

Talk to people
This includes friends, parents, teachers and people who have experience or knowledge that might help (Fig. 1). Visiting people or inviting them into school can be a great help with some projects. How could a cassette recorder be useful?

Look in the shops
Shops are full of ideas by professional designers (Fig. 2). Not all of them are good ones but you might see something that gives *you* a useful idea. Some shops have free catalogues. Pictures that might help should be added to your folder.

Use your library and museums
These are full of objects and ideas. Explain to one of the staff what you are trying to do and you will get plenty of help. Asking saves a lot of time.

Any other ideas?
Ideas are all round you (Fig. 3). Television, advertising, magazines and video bombard us with ideas.

Nature has been working on her designs for millions of years. Animals, plants and other natural things often look good and work well.

Use your imagination
The magic ingredient that can turn all these into design ideas is **imagination.** As a designer you need to look at what is around you. Even more important is being able to imagine how things *might* be.

Fig. 1 **Talk to people:** discuss your idea with others. Sarah talked to her parents.

Fig. 2 **Look in the shops:** John visited a toy shop for ideas.

Fig. 3 **Use your imagination** and look out for ideas.

> *Write down where you could go and who you could talk to if you were give John and Sarah's project.*

Writing for help

There are lots of places you can write to for help with your projects. A wide range of leaflets, pictures and information is available *free*. Fig. 1 shows a letter that Sarah wrote. A well written letter will encourage the reader to take your request seriously. Here are some hints.

1 Say clearly *what* you would like and explain *why*. Be polite and business-like.

2 Send a large envelope for their reply. Remember to put a stamp on and address it clearly to yourself.

3 Arrange to share material with friends. This saves postage and avoids bothering people with lots of requests for the same information.

4 Ask for two copies if you might want to mount the material in a folder or on a wall. Can you work out why two copies are needed?

5 Be patient; the person you are writing to may be very busy.

6 Ask your English teacher for advice on letter writing.

1 *Think of a CDT project you might need information or pictures for and write a practice letter asking for help. Use Sarah's letter to help you.*
2 *Draw and correctly address an envelope for your letter.*

Mrs R. Smith
Tinytots Playgroup
Angley Hall
Tech Town
WORFORDSHIRE
WO 1A

Teachers Phone Nº..
At School 1234
Ext 2

Class 2B
CDT Department
Bingley School
Techtown
Worfordshire

3rd May 198 –

Dear Mrs. Smith,

As part of our work in Craft, Design, Technology (CDT) our class has been asked to design something that will interest young children.

We wonder if you can help us in the following ways :–

(1) May we visit your playgroup to talk to you, the children and their parents?

(2) Will you give us the addresses of organisations and companies that might send us pictures and information?

We have already thought about making our projects safe, but we would welcome your advice. In return we expect to provide your children with new exciting pieces of equipment.

You will be welcome to visit us to discuss this or to see the work in progress.

Yours sincerely,

John King   Sarah Peters

I enclose SAE   on behalf of Class 3B

When you know *what* is needed — how can you provide it?

The questions you ask, and the information you gather should start to give you ideas about what is needed. John and Sarah found out that young children like *movement, bright colours, different textures* and *sounds*. They also worked out the dangers that must be avoided. Once you know *what* is needed you can begin to work out *how* your design will provide it.

First ideas

In Fig. 1 John and Sarah began to work out *how* their project might move, make noises, be coloured and feel interesting. Only a few of their ideas are shown here. Sometimes they used **models** as a quick and cheap way of seeing if an idea would work. A model that works can be used to decide the size and shape of a real project part.

Safety

They decided that **safety** was very important. Toddlers' parents and a playgroup leader agreed and pointed out possible dangers. Figure 2 shows some of the ways they thought of to make the project safe.

Draw another way they could make part of their project move. Look at chapter 6 if you need help.

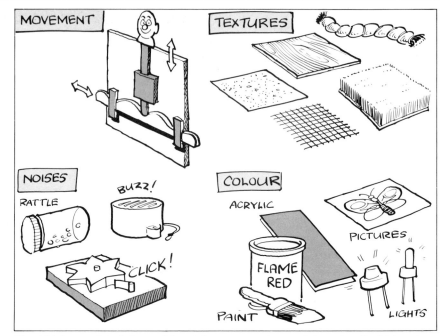

Fig. 1 **Make models:** John and Sarah began to make models and collect ideas to make their project interesting to young children.

Fig. 2 **Safety:** here are some of the ways John and Sarah tried to avoid the dangers they thought of on page 8.

Coming up with possible answers

The next stage is to work out *several* designs. You might think of something absolutely new. You might come up with better versions of old ideas. Use the ideas you have collected; this is not the same as copying. Be adventurous but *remember,* just because something is different it doesn't mean it's better! Check back to the design brief.

Why do you need more than one design?

Your first idea may not be the best. Even if you think it is the best you can do, draw others to make sure.

Your teacher may see snags in your first idea, so have others in reserve. The design you decide to make can include the best parts of your other ideas.

Drawing more than one idea gives *other people* some choice. Professional designers always offer their customers a range of ideas to choose from.

Sketches and drawings

Quick sketches are useful for working out your ideas but you will need clear drawings to show your teacher and other interested people. Chapter 2 will help you with communicating your ideas.

Use this book!

The drawings on this page show how John and Sarah used this book to work out several design ideas. Make sure you use it to help you!

1 *Which of John and Sarah's designs would you choose to make? Say why.*
2 *Make up your own version. You could use the best parts from each of theirs. Draw your idea.*

Fig. 1 **Use this book!** John and Sarah used it to help them produce the design ideas below.

Fig. 2 Page 103 helped with this idea.

Fig 3 Page 119 helped with this idea.

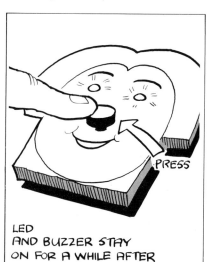

Fig 4 Page 113 helped with this idea.

LED
AND BUZZER STAY
ON FOR A WHILE AFTER
NOSE HAS BEEN PRESSED

Fig 5 This design includes sounds, sights, texture and movement — no battery is needed.

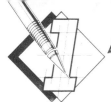

A final solution — the finished design

Your final solution is the one you decide to make. It might be one of your possible solutions or include the best parts of several of them. Check the brief again to be sure your design will do what is needed.

Can you afford to make it?
Have you enough time?
Can you get the parts and materials to make this design?

Developing your design

If all the answers are 'Yes' the idea will need to be **developed.** This means making good drawings that show you have worked out exactly what it will be like. Here are some details you should include:

1 Any important sizes. How long, how wide, how high is it?

2 What will it be made of? Are parts made from different materials? Give reasons why.

3 How will it be made and will any special parts be needed?

4 How will it be finished?

5 How will it be used? Do you need to provide instructions for the user?

Plan how you will make it

1 Will you need to learn any new skills or methods?

2 What will you do *first*? Cleaning up the inside of a box, for example, is best done before it is put together.

3 How will you make best use of your time? For example, can you do something on one piece while glue is drying on another?

4 When you are working with a partner, who will do what?

Fig. 1 **Developing your design:** John and Sarah drew a detailed drawing of their final solution.

Fig. 2 **Plan how you will make it:** John and Sarah made this list.

Take two of the things on John and Sarah's list in Fig. 1 and show what you think that sheet would look like.

Making your project — 'realisation'

So you have decided what your design will be like and planned how it will be made. Having checked with your teacher, you can start making it. This is sometimes called **realisation,** which means **making it real.**

A good project is well designed *and* well made. Your project can fail to do it's job if it is not properly made. It might even be a nuisance or harmful and often looks ugly too. Your teacher and this book will help you get it right, but care and patience are essential.

▌ Make it safely
Most people really enjoy using tools and seeing their design take shape. Follow all safety instructions carefully and you will be able to go on getting better and better.

Page 61 has some important tips on safety which you should read carefully.

So have fun making your project, safely. You could be creating something that will help people and give pleasure for a long time and it will be the only one quite like it!

Look through chapters 4, 5, 6 and list pages that would help Sarah and John make their project shown on page 13.

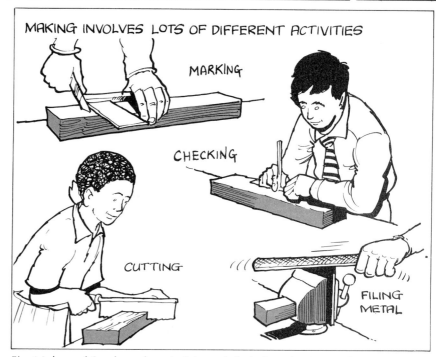

Fig. 1 John and Sarah mark material carefully before shaping it. They join it well because the toddlers may give it rough treatment. They check with their teacher before cutting and use this book to remind them of methods have have been shown.

Fig. 2 They make sure that all corners and edges are rounded. This makes the activity centre safer and nicer to handle. Next they will use paint and varnish to make it attractive and easy to clean. Some pieces are easier to do before you put them together.

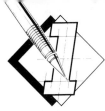

How successful have you been? — testing and 'evaluation'

Finally, you need to find out if your project answers the problem you started with. Ask yourself does it work well and look good in use? Designers do this because they are always trying to improve things. Ask yourself what do I like best about it? How could I make it better? What would I do differently if I did it again? Write a report for your folder. Small changes or modifications may be needed. Very few designs are perfect, even yours!

Ask questions

Here are some of the things John and Sarah wanted to know about their project:

Do the children like it? How can we tell?

How well has it stood up to being used? Do any parts need changing?

What do the parents or playgroup leader think? What do they like about it and have there been any snags?

Use your design folder

Your teacher will want to see how successful you have been too. The ideas in your design folder are as important as the project. Even the ideas you didn't use should be shown. Say why they were rejected. When you show your parents or anybody else your project, be sure to show the design folder too. You deserve credit for all the thinking you've done!

> 1 Design a detailed checklist of questions to ask the users of this project.
> 2 How will questions you ask children differ from those you ask adults?

Fig. 1 A proud moment. John and Sarah's class present their activity centres to the playgroup. A reporter from their local newspaper has been invited.

Fig. 2 They go back later to find out how well they have done and if anything needs improving. They use a cassette recorder so they can write a report later.

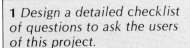

Questions

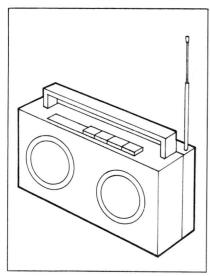

Question 1

1 Imagine that you are about to buy a new portable stereo cassette player.

1.1 Describe the good and bad points you would look for in the many designs on offer. You should think about looks as well as good performance and safety. Draw one you would like.

1.2 Some people find the usual controls hard to use. Design some special controls to help one of the following people:

(a) a young child who wants to play story tapes but can't read what the controls do;

(b) the victim of a motorbike crash who has little strength in his hands and can't grip small things.

1.3 What do you think the portable entertainments of the future will be like? Draw your ideas in the form of an advertisement.

Question 2

2 Your local Parents and Toddlers group have asked your school to design and make some play equipment that will encourage imaginative exploring and exercise. There is a competition to find the best design.

Money is in short supply but they have four sheets of thick plywood that used to be table tops. These are to be your main material. The drawing above gives you an idea of their size.

2.1 Write one list of questions you would want to ask the adults and another you would want to ask the toddlers.

2.2 Draw some ideas for them to choose from. Pay special attention to safety but make your ideas fun.

2.3 Make a model of your best idea using card. Start with four pieces of card the same shape as the plywood in the picture.

3 As you become more experienced at designing you will be encouraged to find your own design problems to solve. Here is a chance to practise doing this.

3.1 Use words and pictures to set out a design problem you would like to tackle. Choose a problem you have actually had or noticed, if you can.

A **design brief** should explain the problem clearly without being too long.

3.2 Do an **analysis**. Write down the important questions you would need to ask about your problems before you could solve it (e.g. How many . .? What size is . .? Does it need to . .?).

3.3 **Research** How would you go about getting the particular answers and information that would help you?

3.4 **Solutions** Draw some ideas that might solve the problem and explain the best one in more detail.

3.5 Imagine you have made your best idea. Explain how you would **test** it to find out if the problem was solved.

4 A pet hamster has escaped.

4.1 Draw some ideas for a trap that will catch the hamster unharmed.

4.2 Draw ideas for an alarm that will tell you when the hamster has been caught.

4.3 Perhaps the hamster escaped because it was bored. Draw some ideas for a hamster adventure playground. Use a variety of materials. Think about safety.

How do I present my ideas?

This is the studio where this book was designed and put together. The designers produced a page design, typeset the text, drew the artwork, and stuck everything down as 'final artwork' for the printer.

Working out your ideas and explaining them to others

We are surrounded by pictures, drawings and symbols because they are a fast, effective and eye-catching way of getting ideas across. There are maps, road signs, car repair manuals, and advertising. Can you think of other examples?

▌Drawing
Drawing is an important part of designing your projects and explaining your ideas.
Sometimes a picture really can be worth a thousand words.

▌Drawings to work out ideas
Like written notes that only you need to understand, this kind of drawing is quick. Some details can be left out because *you* know what you mean. Drawing like this is a good way to sort out ideas in your mind but it is not usually clear enough to tell other people about them.

▌Drawings to show other people your ideas
Clearer drawings, which take longer to do but leave nothing out, are used to show your ideas to others. They should not have to guess what you mean! You may need detailed drawings to:
● get their advice or agreement
● explain how you will solve a problem
● show how a project will look
● impress somebody!
This chapter will help you.

Fig. 1 We are surrounded by pictures and graphic images.

Fig. 2 Drawings to work out ideas.

Fig. 3 Drawings to show other people your ideas.

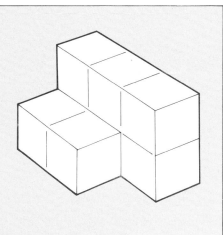

1 *Write a complete description of this block. Time yourself.*
2 *Draw a copy of the block. You may use grid paper to help (p. 22). Again, time yourself.*
3 *Which took the longest, the writing or the drawing?*
4 *Which gives the best idea of the original block, writing or drawing?*
5 *Which is the quickest to understand, writing or drawing?*

Graphics equipment to help you

There are all sorts of things to help you put your ideas on paper.
These range from the simple pencil to the computer.

Collect your own **graphics tool kit.** Most of the things shown here are
easy to get and quite cheap to buy.

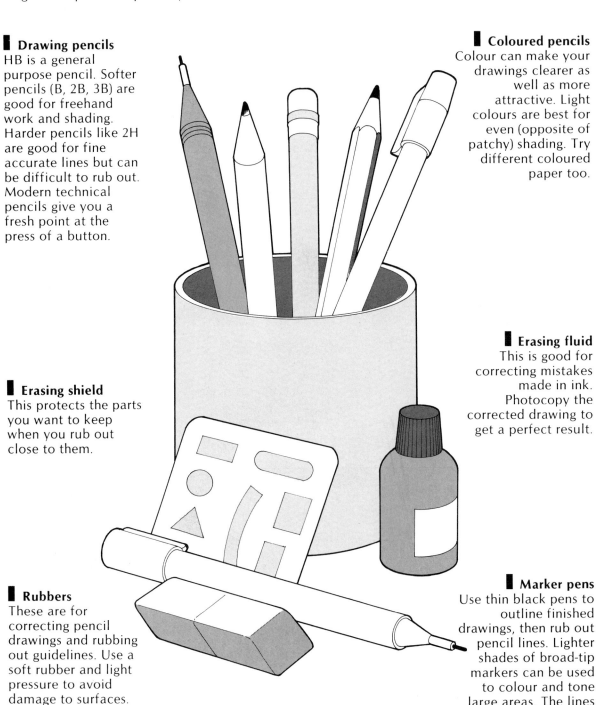

▌ Drawing pencils
HB is a general purpose pencil. Softer pencils (B, 2B, 3B) are good for freehand work and shading. Harder pencils like 2H are good for fine accurate lines but can be difficult to rub out. Modern technical pencils give you a fresh point at the press of a button.

▌ Coloured pencils
Colour can make your drawings clearer as well as more attractive. Light colours are best for even (opposite of patchy) shading. Try different coloured paper too.

▌ Erasing shield
This protects the parts you want to keep when you rub out close to them.

▌ Erasing fluid
This is good for correcting mistakes made in ink. Photocopy the corrected drawing to get a perfect result.

▌ Rubbers
These are for correcting pencil drawings and rubbing out guidelines. Use a soft rubber and light pressure to avoid damage to surfaces.

▌ Marker pens
Use thin black pens to outline finished drawings, then rub out pencil lines. Lighter shades of broad-tip markers can be used to colour and tone large areas. The lines may blur, so to get a sharp outline it is best to cut your drawing out and mount it.

▮ Drawing board

This gives you a flat, smooth surface that can be tilted to a comfortable angle for drawing (Fig. 1). A board is useful for freehand drawing and essential for accurate work with instruments (Fig. 1).

▮ Holding the paper

The instruments on this page are of little use unless the paper is fixed in one position. The clips shown in Fig. 1 are a common way of doing this.

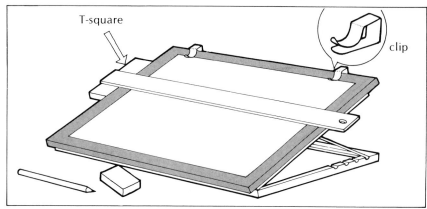

Fig. 1 A drawing board and T-square.

▮ T-square

This is used to draw horizontal lines and to guide and position set-squares and stencils. The **stock** (short part) must be kept tight against the edge of the board when in use.

▮ Set-squares

These are used with the T-square to draw vertical and angular lines. Take care not to chip the edges and keep them clean. An **adjustable** set-square can be set to any angle.

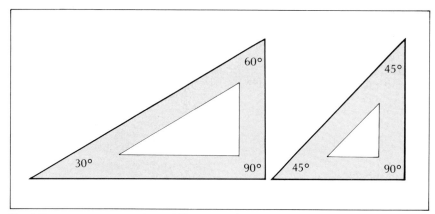

Fig. 2 Two set squares to draw different angles.

▮ Compass and radius template

A **springbow compass** is good for drawing small circles accurately. The **radius template** (Fig. 3(b)) is a quicker way of drawing small circles and arcs. It leaves no holes. Many other templates and stencils are available — letters and ellipses are useful ones to get.

Look in graphic shops and catalogues to see the many other drawing aids available.

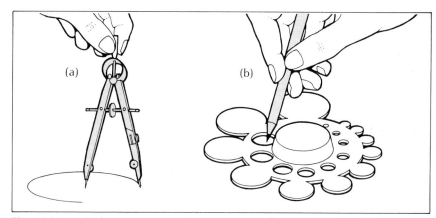

Fig. 3 (a) A springbow compass   (b) A radius template.

---

1 *Using drawing board, set-squares and T-square only, copy these shapes. Add objects of your own design. Make the drawings any convenient size.*
2 *The set-squares in Fig. 2 can be used to draw angles of 90°, 45°, 30° and 60° when used separately. Use them to draw these angles and label them clearly. Check with a protractor if you aren't sure.*
3 *List the angles you could draw by resting one set square against the other.*

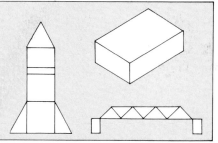

2 Freehand drawing

Freehand drawing is a quick way of working out ideas and explaining them to others. All you need is a pencil and paper. More formal drawings, using T-squares and other instruments, should be worked out freehand first.

Like all skills, freehand drawing takes practice. Below are some ways to improve your freehand drawing.

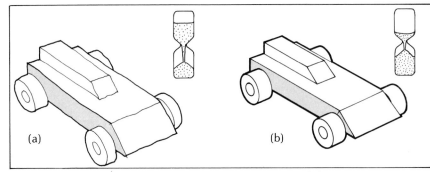

Fig. 1 Fig 1(a) Freehand   (b) Using instruments. Which took longer?

How to draw lines

Figure 2 shows the right and the wrong way to draw lines. Try to make all your lines *clean* rather than *hairy*. This is often easier if you draw quite quickly. Practise drawing clean straight lines, starting with short ones.

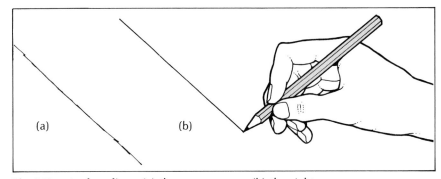

Fig. 2 **How to draw lines:** (a) the wrong way   (b) the right way.

Getting the lines to go where you want them to is important. Make a dot and practise drawing lines to it (Fig. 3). Use one smooth movement starting close the dot.

How to draw parallel lines

Practise drawing one line parallel to another (Fig. 4). Concentrate on the last line you drew, rather than watching your pencil point. The further apart the lines are, the more difficult this becomes.

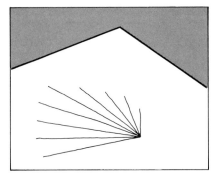

Fig. 3 **How to draw lines:** practise drawing to a point.

Fig. 4 **Drawing parallel lines:** concentrate on the last line you drew.

How to draw circles

To sketch a circle, first draw a square for it to fit into (Fig. 5). Drawing smooth circles takes practice. Start with small ones.

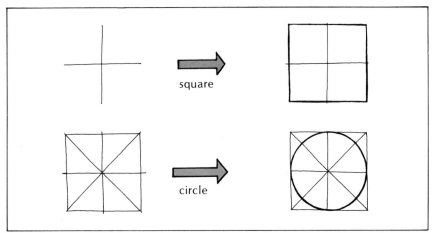

square

circle

Fig. 5 **Drawing circles:** draw a square first.

Construction lines

Difficult objects can be made easier to draw by building them on faint boxes or **construction lines.** When an object is symmetrical, like this board game counter (Fig. 6), draw a line down the centre first. Draw construction lines *lightly* so that they are easy to rub out when the drawing is finished. Make sure the construction lines look right before drawing the actual object.

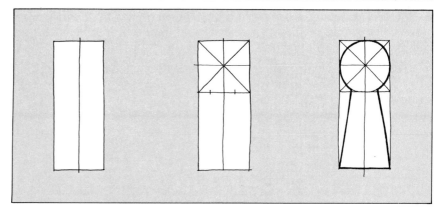

Fig. 6 **Construction lines** and the finished drawing.

Fig. 7 Many projects you design will include box shapes. Practise until you can draw them well.

Grid paper

Graph paper and **isometric grid paper** can improve your freehand drawing a lot (Fig. 9). Simply clip thin drawing paper over the grid so that you can use the grid lines to help you. (See p. 25 and p. 26.)

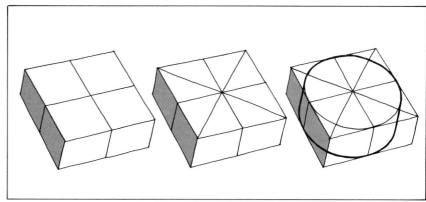

Fig. 8 Boxes can help with tricky shapes. Get the box right first.

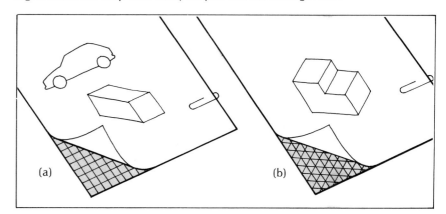

Fig. 9 **Grid paper:** drawing paper clipped over grids (a) orthographic or oblique (b) isometric.

1(a) Copy the construction lines in Fig. 6 feintly, then draw in the board game counter shown.
(b) Use the same method to draw a different counter from the same board game.
2(a) Try drawing boxes seen from different angles. (See Fig. 7.)
(b) Draw some more boxes with square ends and use them as guidelines to draw cylinders like the one in Fig. 8.
3 Use the graph or grid paper method to draw simple objects or projects of your choice.

2 One point perspective

Perspective drawings are used in books, magazines and advertising material. You can use them too. After working on these pages you will probably be able to spot examples.

In perspective drawing, as in real life, things seem smaller the further away they are. You may have noticed this when looking down a long straight path (Fig. 1).

The example below shows how easy it is to get good results.

Fig. 1 Looking down a path.

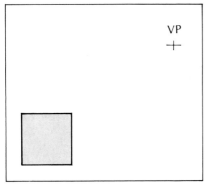

1 To draw a block, first draw a square. Then mark a **vanishing point** (v.p.).

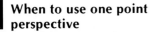

2 Draw feint lines to the v.p. from the points shown. Hold the pencil lightly and near the top.

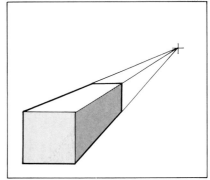

3 Decide how long you want the block to be and draw in it's edges. Don't go too close to the v.p. unless you want a lot of **distortion.**

When to use one point perspective

One point perspective can be used to plan rooms, window displays and stage scenes. You could use it to show what your project would look like in a particular setting. In Fig. 2 we are looking into a room.

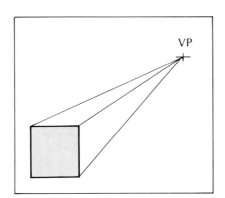

Fig. 2 Looking into a room.

1 Draw blocks using the method shown in 1 — 3 above. Try putting the v.p. in different positions each time. Shade them to make them look real. Decide which will be the darkest and lightest sides.

2 Copy the room shown in Fig. 2. Try adding carpets and other fittings. You could also design a room for yourself.
3 Try drawing letters like those opposite. Square styles are easiest. Draw the front of the letter first.

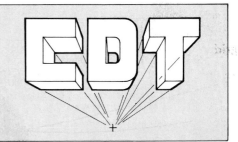

Two point perspective

Here you use two vanishing points (v.p.) but the method is similar to one point perspective.

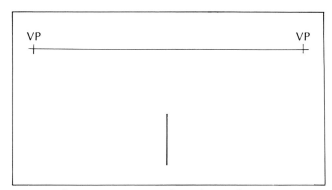

1 Mark two v.p.'s near the edges of your paper. Then draw a vertical line below them. This will be the nearest edge of your box.

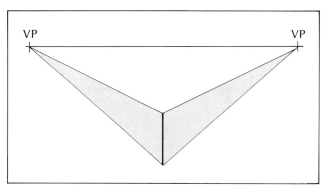

2 Draw feint lines from the top and bottom of your vertical line to each v.p.

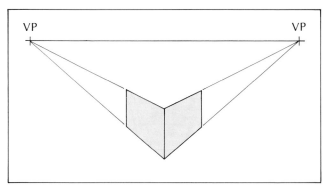

3 Add two vertical lines where you want the box to end.

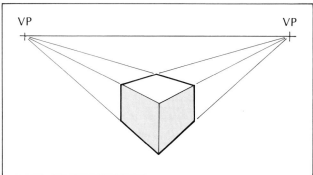

4 Draw a line from each corner to it's v.p. to finish the box. Go over the lines you want to keep. Turn your paper upside down and you will seem to see the box underneath.

▌ How to draw a project

To draw an actual project, remember these points:

● The further below the v.p. line you start, the more the *top* of the object will be seen.

● The closer to the v.p. you work the more your drawing will *taper*. A lot of taper can make an object look big.

● Start with the front corner.

● Use the v.p.'s, don't start guessing angles.

● With the help of boxes, curves can be drawn freehand.

● When you want your drawing to fill the whole page, put the v.p.'s on a separate, larger backing sheet.

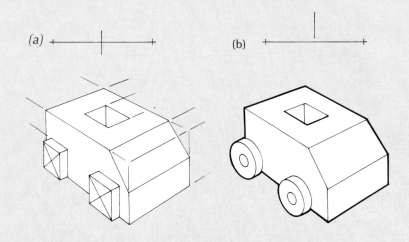

1 Draw the box in 1 – 4 above following the stages shown.
2 Draw more boxes but put the vertical starting line like this:

(a)

(b)

3 Use this method to draw a simple wheeled toy based on a block. Draw boxes to help you put in the wheels freehand.

3D drawing — oblique

Most people find 2D drawing quite easy. Oblique drawing is a way of turning 2D drawings into 3D ones that give more information. Below left are three ways of producing the drawing shown in **1** to **3** below right.

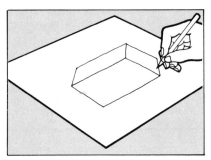

Freehand, using only a pencil.

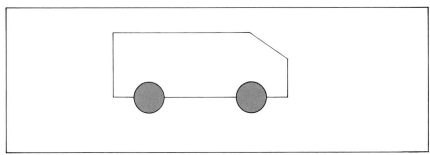

1 Do a 2D drawing first. Put circles and parts of circles on this so that you can use a compass.

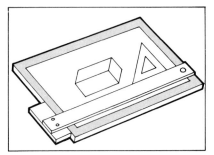

Using a 45° set-square, T-square and board.

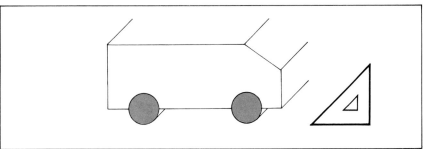

2 Draw in the sloping lines at 45° but make them half their real size or the drawing will look wrong.

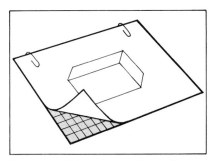

Draw on thin paper clipped over graph paper.

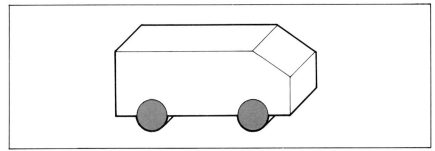

3 Join up the lines to finish.

Use thin drawing paper clipped over graph paper to do the following (Choose sizes that suit your paper.):

1 *Follow the stages in* **1-3** *above and draw the vehicle shown. Add windows and other details.*
2 *Draw the front view of the letter E, then finish it as an oblique drawing.*
3*Draw the shape shown opposite and then make it into a 3D object. Use a compass.*

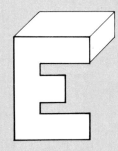

3D drawing — isometric

Here is another way of drawing your projects in 3D, even if you are not a great artist. **Isometric drawing** can be done with a drawing board, T-square and 30° set-square (Fig. 1a). A quicker and less formal drawing can be made by using grid paper to guide your lines (Fig. 1b). The grid must be used as shown *with its vertical lines running up and down the paper.*

Even complicated shapes can be drawn by starting with a feintly drawn box. When the drawing is complete you can rub out any lines you don't need and go over the ones you want.

Stages 1 to 5 below show you how to draw the vehicle body shown on page 25.

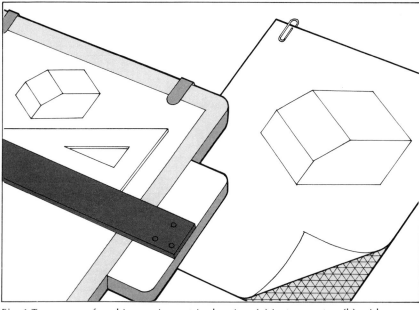

Fig. 1 Two ways of making an isometric drawing: (a) instruments (b) grid paper.

1 Draw a feint vertical line to show how high the object is. This is the front corner of your box.

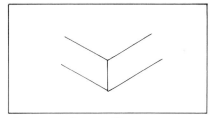

2 Draw lines off at 30° using the 30° set square or grid lines to help.

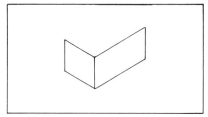

3 Put in more vertical lines to show how long and how wide the object is.

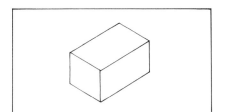

4 Use the 30° set square or grid lines to put in the back corner and finish the box.

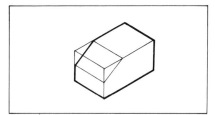

5 Put in lines to show how far back and how far down this slope goes. Join them up down the side.

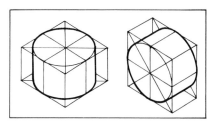

6 Circles and parts of them can be drawn by drawing isometric boxes and sketching them inside.

Using grid paper under your drawing sheet or a drawing and 30° set square:

1 Draw the vehicle body by following the steps shown. Add wheels and other details.
2 Design your own vehicle using the same method. Keep it simple.
3 Draw isometric boxes and other objects of your choice. Try both methods (Fig. 1) if equipment is available.

Looking at the project one side at a time — orthographic drawing

Sometimes it is easier and clearer to draw your project seen from one direction at a time (Fig. 1). Drawings of this kind are often used in industry to give exact details of an object. Although often done with a drawing board and instruments, useful **orthographic drawings** can be done freehand or helped by graph paper clipped under your drawing paper.

The position of the different views is important. Anyone who knows this way of drawing can tell which is the front or side of an object just by where it is drawn. Notice the thin construction lines that help the views line up with each other.

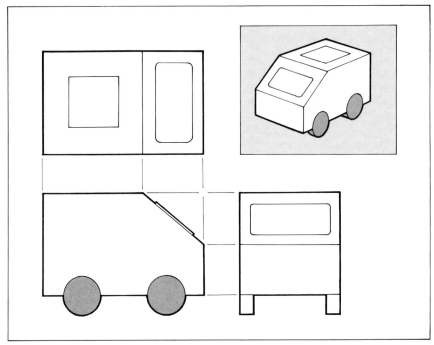

Fig. 1 An orthographic drawing of a project.

Copy these orthographic drawings and add the missing views.
The squares are to help you copy; you don't need to draw them.
Graph paper clipped under your drawing sheet will make this easier.

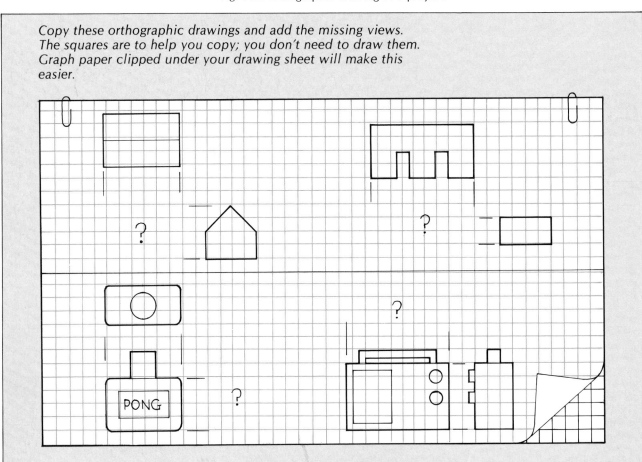

Showing sizes on your drawings

Sometimes you will want to show sizes on your drawings. Here are some examples (Fig. 1) and a few tips to help you.

● Keep sizes outside the outline of the object.

● Lines that show sizes should be drawn thin.

● Write figures so that they are easy to read without turning the drawing round.

● Check that you have given all the information that is needed but don't clutter up the drawing.

▌ Make a list of parts
You will often find it helpful to list the parts needed for a project. You might do this to show your teacher what materials you need or to work out the cost of a project. Fig. 2 shows a good way to lay out such a list.

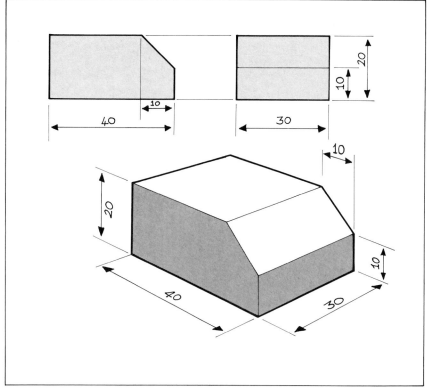

Fig. 1 Add sizes to your drawings. Keep them clear of the drawing lines.

ACTIVITY CENTRE BOX   (ALL SIZES IN MILLIMETRES)

NAME	No.	L	W	Th	MATERIAL
SIDES	2	300	30	30	PINE
ENDS	2	200	30	30	PINE
TOP	1	300	200	3	PLYWOOD
BOTTOM	1	300	200	3	PLYWOOD

Fig. 2 **Make a list of parts:** here is one example.

---

1 *Sketch some simple objects such as shaped blocks and add important sizes.*
2 *Draw a parts list like the one shown (Fig. 2) but give the sizes for a smaller box.*

Exploded drawings

This is a way of showing objects as if they were pulled apart (Fig. 1). You may have seen instruction sheets or model kit plans like this. Look out for examples.

Exploded drawing is a useful way of explaining how your project will be put together or how it will work.

Drawings like this can be done freehand or using one of the other ways of 3D drawing shown in this chapter. Isometric (p. 26) is often used. When drawing with instruments, it is best to do a freehand sketch first to work things out.

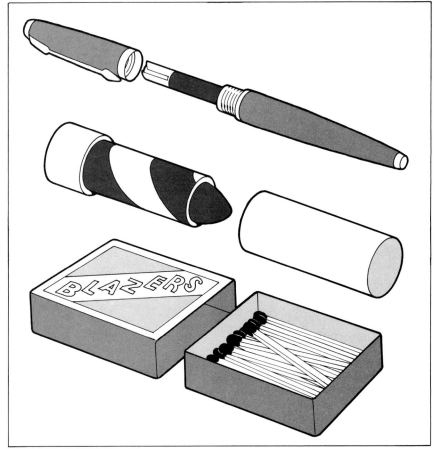

Fig. 1 Lots of things are taken apart in everyday use. Can you think of other examples?

Clip isometric grid paper under your drawing sheet (p. 26) before you start.

1 *Draw these objects exploded. The arrows show how to pull them apart.*
2 *Draw three building bricks that would fit together. Show them* exploded.
3 *List some objects that can be taken apart. Choose one that you know well or can have in front of you and draw it* exploded.

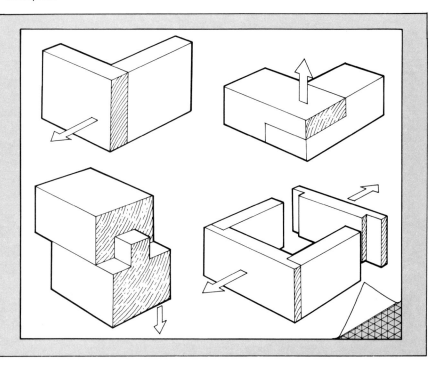

Make your work stand out with 'thick and thin' line

Look at the drawing in Figs. 1 and 2. You will probably agree that Fig. 2 looks better than Fig. 1. Can you see what makes the difference?

In Fig. 1 all lines are the *same* thickness, but in Fig. 2 some lines are *thick* and others *thin*.

Technical illustrators use this method and you can use it to improve your design drawings.

▌ How to use this method

We use lines to show where two surfaces meet. When one of the surfaces is out of sight, like here, the line is **thick.**

When you can see both the surfaces that a line joins, like here, the line should be drawn **thin.**

Look at Fig. 3 again. How would the thick and thin line change if this block were resting on a table top?

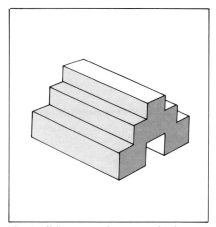

Fig. 1 All lines are the same thickness.

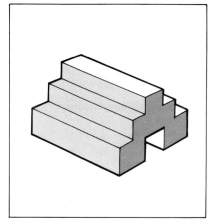

Fig. 2 Drawing with thick and thin lines.

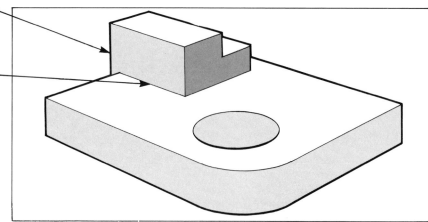

Fig. 3 Blocks drawn with thick and thin lines.

1 Copy the block in Fig. 2. The difference between thick and thin lines should be clear but not overdone.

2 Using thin paper clipped over isometric grid paper, draw these blocks faintly. They are made up of 1cm cubes. (See page 26 if you need help. Add thick and thin lines. (Don't draw the dotted lines.)

3 Design some blocks of your own using the same method as in question 2. Add thick and thin line.

4 Collect examples of this technique. These should be easy to find as most technical illustrations use it. Model kit plans and instruction manuals are good places to look.

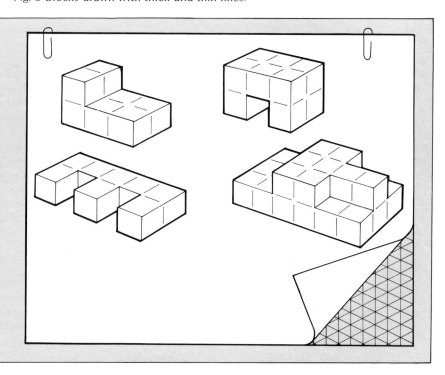

What is it made of?

Showing what something is made from gives important information as well as improving the look of your drawings. Labels could be used, but shading the surfaces in various ways gives a better idea of what the object will be like (Fig. 1).

There are many ways of drawing different materials. Here are a few to try.

▌How to draw wood
There are many different timbers and a number of ways of drawing them. Two methods are shown in Fig. 2. Don't make the grain markings too dark or they will distract the viewer from the outline of the object.

The growth rings that show on the **end grain** must not be drawn touching or crossing. They run right through a piece, like letters through seaside rock.

The layers that make up plywood are shown as lines. They should be drawn *lighter* than the outline and with some gaps, especially on the edge getting most light.

▌How to draw metal
Metals are usually smooth and shiny. They *reflect* lots of light. Decide which side most light is coming from as this helps you get lightest and darkest parts right on each part of the drawing (Fig. 3). The brightest areas are known as **highlights.** One way to show them is to leave small gaps in the outline.

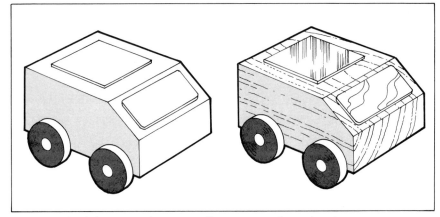

Fig. 1 Which of these two drawings tells you most about the object?

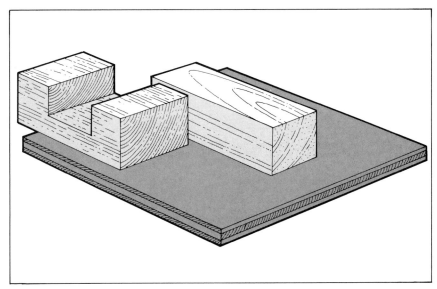

Fig. 2 **How to draw wood:** some examples.

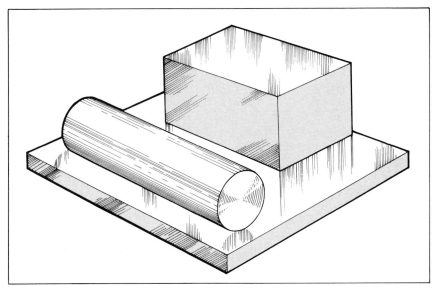

Fig. 3 **How to draw metal:** some examples.

▌ Glass and clear plastics

These materials are transparent and reflect a lot of light (Fig. 4). Objects seen through them should be drawn *fainter* than usual.

▌ Coloured plastics

Some kinds are more shiny than others (Fig. 5). **Acrylic** (perspex) reflects a lot of light. Put in **highlights** where most light is reflected. These are most noticeable on *darker* colours.

▌ Softer materials

Expanded polystyrene

This is made up of small beads (Fig. 6). Show them by drawing small circles with gaps in them. Draw more on darker parts of the object. Give it slightly crumbly edges.

Upholstery foam and pipe insulation

Draw the shape very faintly then pick out the outline with dots (Fig. 6).

Hard rubber

Use a normal line to draw the object, then put dots on its surface (Fig. 6). Put plenty of dots in the darkest places changing gradually to none at all in the lightest areas.

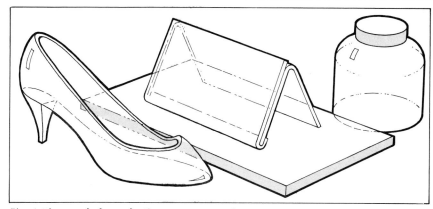

Fig. 4 **Glass and clear plastics:** some examples.

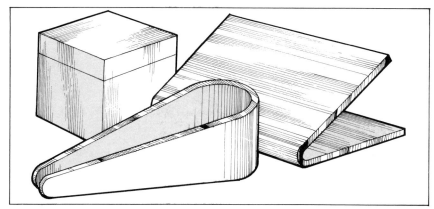

Fig. 5 **Coloured plastics:** acrylic is one example.

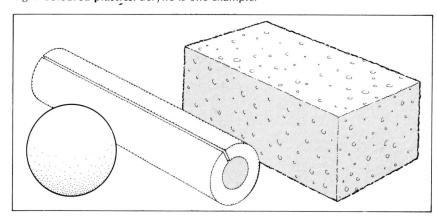

Fig. 6 **Softer materials:** rubber (left), foam (middle), expanded polystyrene (right).

1 *Draw six cubes. Make them as large as will comfortably fit on your paper. Make each look like one of the eight different materials shown. You should not need to label them!*
2 *Ask a friend if they can tell which cube represents which material.*
3 *There are many ways of showing different materials. Collect examples from books, advertisements and magazines. Cut out or photocopy a variety and use them to improve your own technique.*

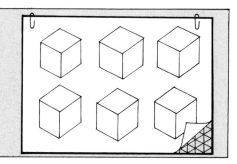

How to design your own symbols

A **symbol** is a simplified way of presenting a thing or an idea. Fig. 1 gives you some examples. Imagine how much longer it would take to draw the lifelike versions. Well-designed symbols are quick and easy to understand, even from a distance. Many road signs, instructions and warning notices include symbols. You can use them in design drawings and projects.

How to design your own symbols

1 Write down and draw the information you want to put across.

2 Draw the information again but concentrate on what matters most, get rid of anything that's not essential. One way to simplify the design is to cut it out of coloured paper.

3 Before including your symbol in a project, test it on other people. Do they understand what your symbol means? Could it mean more than one thing? Can you make it more simple and easy to understand?

Fig. 1 Some symbols in common use.

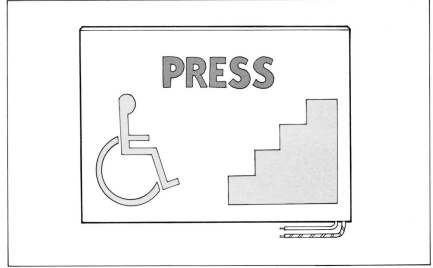

Fig. 2 Symbols can be used on membrane panel switches (p.111) to show what happens when they are pressed. Perhaps you can think of other projects when symbols would help.

1 *Design a symbol to be put on the lid of a box. This should make it clear what is to be kept inside, and be simple and attractive.*
2 *A department store is used by many foreign visitors some of whom do not speak English. Design symbols to show what is for sale on each floor.*
3 *Design symbols for a trophy, key-ring or piece of jewellery*
4 *Collect examples of symbols to put in your design folder.*

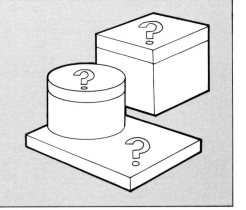

Enlarging and reducing

This is useful when you have a shape you like but need a larger or smaller copy of it. The hen toy and puzzle in Fig. 1 is an example of the same shape being needed in different sizes. Using this method you could even enlarge a postcard-sized picture to cover a wall! The original drawing or picture has to be divided into squares. This is best done on *tracing paper* which you then clip over the design. The more squares you use, the more accurate the copy.

Fig. 1 Shapes can be copied exactly but in different sizes.

1 Draw or find the shape you want.

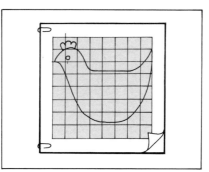

2 Make a grid to fit over your design. Trace this from squared paper. The grid can be used lots of times.

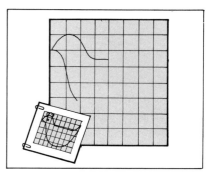

3 Draw another grid on drawing paper, the right size to fit the shape as you want it to be, with the same number of squares as your first grid.

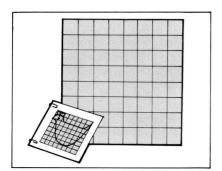

4 Copy your shape onto the second grid one square at a time.

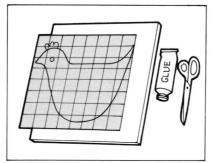

5 When you plan to use the shape lots of times or want to draw round it, you can stick it on card and use it as a template.

6 When you only want to use the shape once, you can trace or stick it on the material to be cut.

1 Draw a grid 120mm wide and 100mm high. Each square should have 20mm sides. Use squared paper to save time.
2 Copy the hen shape from number 3 above onto your grid. How many times bigger will you have made it?
3 Find a shape in a book or magazine. Enlarge or reduce it following the stages shown on this page.

Photocopying

Most schools have a photocopier and they can also be used in some libraries and shops. You can use one to present ideas, save time and improve the quality of your work.

Here are some ideas:

1 When copied, clear pencil lines become much blacker. A pencil drawing can be copied so that it looks as good as an ink drawing. Rubbing out and other blemishes vanish.

2 One drawing can be used to do several different jobs. You could use one copy for wall display, one copy for a folder cover and you still have your original.

3 You could draw a vehicle body without wheels. Different wheel designs could be added to each copy. This way you only need to draw the vehicle body once.

4 Some copiers can reduce drawings, that is, make them smaller. This can improve a drawing a lot by *sharpening* the lines and hiding small blemishes. Printers and illustrators use this technique.

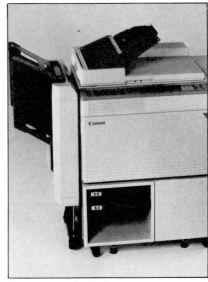

Fig. 1 A standard photocopier.

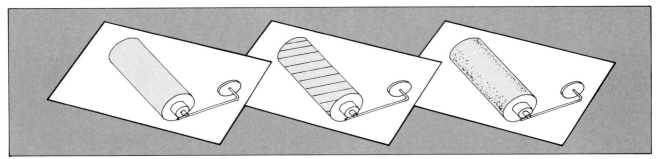

5 Using copies, you can try out and choose the best way of shading and colouring work without risking your original drawing.

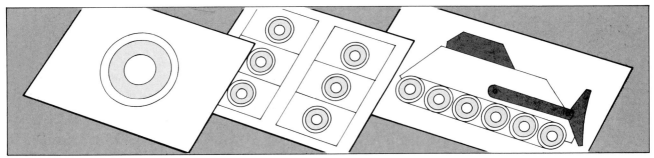

6 When a drawing has lots of parts that are meant to look the same, draw the part once and photocopy the number you need. Use a glue stick to fix them to the rest of the drawing and copy the whole thing.

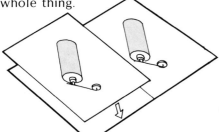

1 *Make copies of one of your pencil drawings and try various ways of shading them. Copy a drawing that has not been coloured or shaded.*
2 *See if you can think of any other CDT uses for the photocopier. Describe your ideas using words and drawings.*

Models and mock-ups

In CDT, a model is a quick and easily made version of your project. You can use models to see how a project will look and whether it will work, before starting on the real thing. Designers use models to avoid expensive and time wasting mistakes.

Any safe material that is cheap and quick to work with can be used.
Use your imagination. Remember, a model should be:

- easy and quick to make.
- strong enough to handle.
- realistic enough for the idea to be judged.

Here are a few ideas about models and mock-ups.

Templates
These are very useful for **symmetrical** shapes such as boat hulls and table tennis bats. A symmetrical shape is one that can be divided down the middle giving two halves the same. To make a template like this, take some thin card big enough for your finished shape. Score and fold it down the middle. Draw *half* your shape along the fold and cut it out. Unfold and draw round the finished template (Fig. 1).

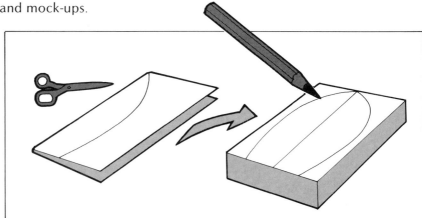
Fig. 1 **Templates:** produce your shape in card and draw round it on the final material.

Moving parts
Using **paper fasteners** and card, it is easy to try out mechanisms. In Fig. 2 an idea for tipping a lorry back is being tried out. Paper fasteners are good for moving joints. **Eyelets** (often used for leatherwork) are even better. A special tool is needed to fix them.

3D card models
These are especially good when you are planning work in acrylic, tinplate or any sheet material. Fig. 3 shows a card model of a desk tidy. More solid shapes like a cube can be built up by cutting, folding and sticking. The flat version, called a **development,** should be worked out on a drawing board or on squared paper stuck to the card.

> **1** Design your own desk tidy by modelling it in thin card.
> **2** Make a card cube using the picture to help you.

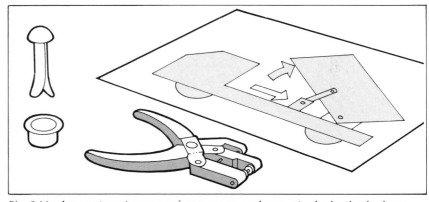
Fig. 2 **Moving parts:** using paper fasteners or eyelets to tip the back of a lorry.

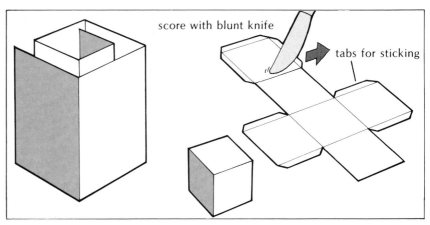
score with blunt knife

tabs for sticking

Fig. 3 **3D card models:** a desk tidy and its development.

Modelling materials

Modelling clay

This is good for modelling solid objects with complicated curves. A handle is a good example. Here's how to model one:

1 Shape the clay until it is the same size and shape as the material you will make the real handle from (Fig. 1(a)).

2 Hold the block as you would the handle and squeeze until the grip is comfortable (Fig. 1(b)).

3 You can now copy the model in wood or use it to make a mould for casting in plastic (Fig. 1(c)).

Wire and welding rod

Thin wire is easy to bend and good for creating shapes for mobiles, jewellery and so on. Thicker wire or welding rod is good for modelling metal frames and other projects to be made from metal rod (Fig. 2). Use thicknesses that you can cut and bend with pliers.

Balsa wood

This is quickly shaped with sharp tools. It is good for modelling wooden projects (Fig. 3).

Construction kits

These are good for working models (Fig. 4). Even complicated ideas can be built quite quickly. Your model can only be kept until the parts are needed for another job.

Models

Models are an important way of thinking out ideas and showing them to other people. Take care of all models and hand them in with the finished project.

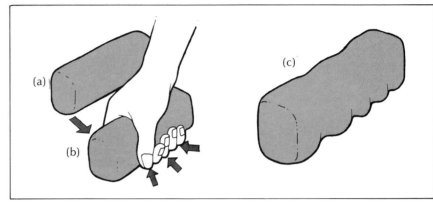

Fig. 1 **Modelling clay:** how to make a handle.

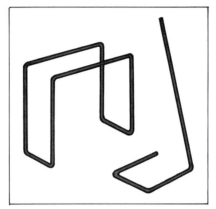

Fig. 2 **Wire and welding rod:** these are easily bent to create shapes and frames.

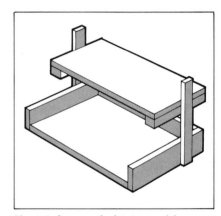

Fig. 3 **Balsa wood:** this is good for modelling wooden projects.

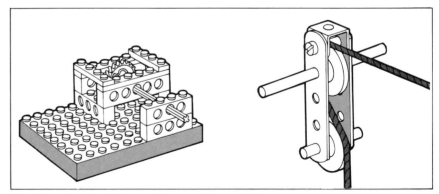

Fig. 4 **Construction kits:** good for working models.

1 Make the folded template for a symmetrical project of your choice. Bats, boat hulls, hand mirror backs and jewellery are some ideas.
2 Draw (and if possible model) another way of tipping the lorry back on p.36.
3 Use stiff paper or thin card to model projects you would like to make in acrylic or metal sheet. It may help to make a folded form first and then think of uses for it.

Presenting your ideas

After drawing and modelling ideas, you need to put them together in a sensible and attractive way. Be sure to show the problem clearly and the stages you went through to solve it (p. 6). Good design work, well displayed, earns a lot of marks in CDT.

Mounting and display methods should be kept simple to focus attention on the work itself (Fig. 1). Try several ways of arranging the work and different coloured backgrounds before you fix anything. Photographs can be very useful (Fig. 4). Here are some more tips:

▌ Double mounting
Fix your work to a slightly larger piece of coloured paper before mounting on a backing sheet (Fig. 2). Try a range of coloured papers until you find two that go well together. Harsh, bright colours are best avoided.

Going round the outline of work with marker pens is another idea to try.

▌ Lettering
Choose a style that suits the work. Avoid fancy letters that are difficult to read. 'Rub on' letters give good results if put on carefully (Fig. 3). The catalogues that advertise them are a good place to look for ideas. Lettering can be done with stencils or freehand. Typewriters and computer printers can also be used for lettering.

> Cut out different sized rectangles of card. They don't need to be large. Use them to practise layouts on a different coloured backing sheet.
>
> Try several arrangements and draw round or stick down the one you think looks best.

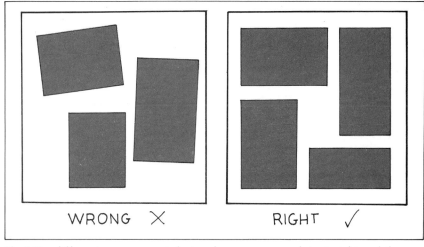

WRONG ✕   RIGHT ✓

Fig. 1 Try different arrangements but make sure your work is straight and the edges line up.

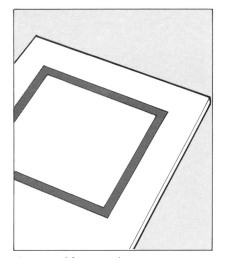

Fig. 2 **Double mounting.**

Fig. 3 **Lettering:** rub on letters, stencils and freehand work.

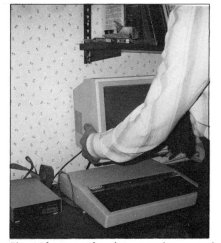

Fig. 4 **Photographs:** these can be a good way of showing design problems and your solutions in use, in this case a stand for a computer screen.

Displaying 3D models and projects

Models and projects will need something to stand on such as tables and benches. Cover them with sugar paper or plain cloth of a suitable colour. Dark objects don't show well against a dark background. Too bright a background may dazzle and distract the viewer.

Experiment with all these ideas to find the best way of showing off your work.

Using different levels
Displaying work on different levels adds interest and prevents things being hidden by what is in front. Boxes, blocks or piles of books covered with cloth can be used.

Backdrops
A backdrop or screen behind the work helps to focus the viewer's attention. This is a good place to display drawings, photographs and small projects. The wrap-round screen shown will stand up on its own if angled enough.

Complementary material
The display of children's beach toys also includes shells, seaweed, and other things found on the seashore. This looks attractive and creates the right atmosphere. Pictures from holiday brochures also help. A tray of sand would add to the effect and people could try out the toys. Collect objects that will add to your displays; making a list might help.

Lighting
This is an important part of window dressing and other professional displays. Putting your project in a pool of light can focus attention on it. Experiment with desk lamps and other adjustable lights.

Fig. 1 A display of work on the theme of 'beach toys'.

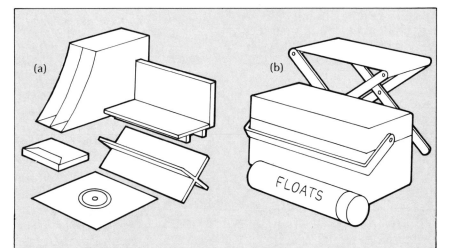

Use drawings and notes to describe how you would display work on the theme of:

(a) single and cassette storage.
(b) river and lake fishing.
or
(c) a theme of your choice.

Include your use of:
1 Different levels. Backdrop and graphics.
2 Lists of complementary objects.
Show more than one idea.

Questions

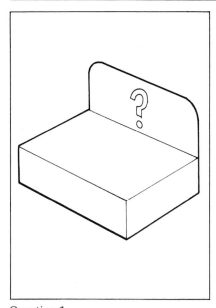

Question 1

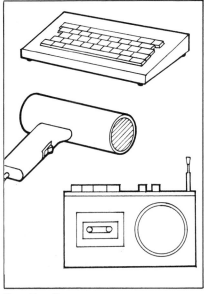

Question 2

Question 3

1 Here is the package for a mystery product.

1.1 Make five freehand drawings of this box to show what it would look like from different angles.

1.2 Draw the box faintly using **two-point perspective** (p. 24). If you are really clever you can also show how it opens.

1.3 Go over your faint drawing using the **thick and thin** lines (p. 30).

1.4 Add important sizes that would suit a box of this shape (p. 28).

2 What do you think belongs in the box in question 1? The drawings above might give you some ideas.

2.1 Work out your idea freehand then make an **oblique** or **isometric** drawing of it. Show what material each part is made from. If you have no grid paper or instruments, do your best freehand.

2.2 Make an **orthographic** drawing (p. 27) of the front, top and one end of the box. Use squared paper or instruments to help if you have them.

2.3 Add suitable lettering and drawings to show what is in the box and make people want it.

2.4 Make up some instructions (mainly drawings) for the back of the box. They could show step-by-step how to use the product, or you might have an **exploded** drawing showing how it goes together. Choose the best method for your product.

3 Draw a 200 mm square and use faint lines to divide it into 20 mm squares. Position this so that you can draw a 50 mm square next to it and divide that into 5 mm squares. Squared paper or a drawing board will help. You will use this grid to help you design the symbols below.

3.1 Which department of a large store would be most likely to sell your product? In the large square, design a **symbol** to help customers find that department.

3.2 A smaller copy of your symbol is needed for display inside a lift. Use the grid method (p. 34) to draw this in the smaller square.

3.3 A copy of your symbol is needed to stand up on a counter or shelf. Draw a cardboard stand that would do the job and use an **exploded drawing** (p. 29) to show how it fixes to the back of the sign.

The *Fineblade* paper to produce one copy of this book comes from pine (softwood) and maple eucalyptus (hardwood) trees. Calcium carbonate and china clay with a latex binder have been added to produce a smooth white surface which is reasonably opaque — it stops the printing showing through on the wrong side of the paper.

We depend on materials in many ways. Our ability to shape and use them is one of the things that makes human beings special.

Think of all the materials you see every day (Fig. 1) and the many different jobs they do. Anyone involved in designing and making needs to know what materials are available and how they behave.

This section helps you get to know the main materials you will use in CDT. This should help you decide which is the best to use for a job when you are designing and making a project. Many materials are becoming scarce which means it is very important to avoid waste and use them sensibly.

▐ Choose carefully!

Choosing the wrong material can cause accidents, discomfort and other problems. Look at the goods on sale in Fig. 2. Would you buy any of them? If your answer is 'no' then you already know quite a lot about materials. After looking at this section you will know even more.

Think up some more awful goods that might be sold on the market stall in Fig. 2. Draw some of them. You will need to decide what a material is good at and what it is bad at to do this. You could start by making a list of different materials.

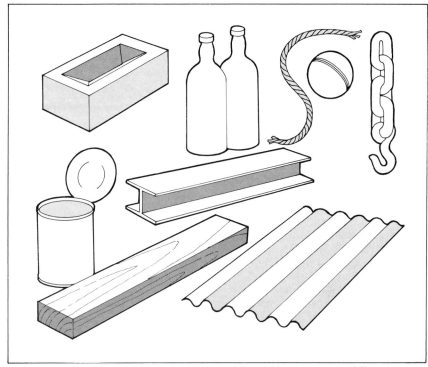

Fig. 1 We use lots of different materials and they help us in many different ways.

Fig. 2 **Choose carefully:** would you buy any of the goods on sale here?

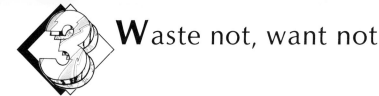
Using materials carefully includes not wasting them by using more than you need to do a job.

How much do you need?

Whether a piece is large enough and strong enough can depend on how you use it (Fig. 1).

The right decisions can make a project cheaper and lighter, yet just as strong (Fig. 2). This project is designed to help a child reach a toilet and wash basin. A thin top makes it light to move but how would you arrange the support underneath to make it most rigid?

Using less material is also kinder to our planet's supply of **raw materials,** or **natural resources.**

What is a beam?

Any piece that has to resist bending can be called a **beam.** Designers aim to produce beams that are strong enough but use as little material as possible. These steel beams (Fig. 3) show how good design can help to conserve the world's materials. Solid ones would use far more material to support the same load. This would make them heavier and more expensive.

Fig. 1 **How much do you need?:** using a beam the right way can make all the difference!

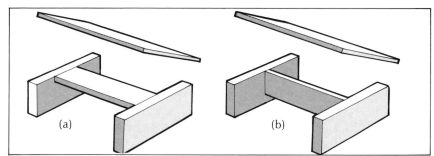

Fig. 2 **How much do you need?:** which way round would you put the supporting beam?

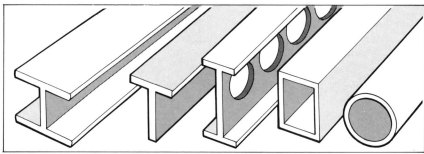

Fig. 3 **What is a beam?:** some well-designed steel beams.

1 *What is the strongest beam you can make from a piece of card? For a fair test, your ideas should be made from pieces the same size and thickness.*
2 *What will you use as a load? It should be something you can measure and increase a bit at a time.*
3 *How will you fix the load on top of your beam or hang it underneath?*
4 *Can you think of another way of testing beams?*
5 *Work out a clear way of recording what happens as you test different designs.*

Fig. 4 Look how the children in this drawing are making their beam. It should give you some ideas for your own designs.

Basic things to know about wood

Wood is the *only* important material that we can grow more of. The problem is that trees are being used up faster than they are being replaced. We should all avoid wasting wood to **conserve** some for the future.

People have been using wood for thousands of years and it is still an important material. You already know what it looks and feels like. You may even be sitting on some right now!

Hardwoods and softwoods
There are many kinds of wood with many different uses. We can divide them into two groups. **Hardwoods** are mostly slow growing and expensive. They come from **broad-leaved** trees (Fig. 1(a)). **Softwood** trees grow faster and have **needles** like Christmas trees (Fig. 1(b)). You will use softwoods like **pine** for most of your projects because they are cheaper and often easier to work with.

Rot and insects
Wood can **rot** or be attacked by some beetles. You can see how to prevent this on p. 53.

Seasoning
Why can't you just cut off a piece of a tree and use it on a project? Like all plants, a freshly cut tree has a lot of water in it. Unless it is dried slowly in a special way called **seasoning,** the wood cracks and twists very badly (Fig. 2). The wood you use on projects may have been seasoned in a special **kiln** (Fig. 3). Some trees are also protected by law — oaks for example.

1 *Fig. 1 shows some things made from wood. Make a list of others. Draw some of them.*
2 *How many kinds of wood can you name? Make a list. Are they hardwoods or softwoods?*

(a)   (b)

Fig. 1 **Hardwoods and softwoods:** a hardwood tree (a), a softwood tree (b) and some of the many things made from wood.

TWIST AND SPLIT

Fig. 2 **Seasoning:** wood from a newly felled tree is no good for most projects.

SEASONING KILN

Fig. 3 **Seasoning:** controlled drying is needed to avoid twisting and splitting.

Grain

A piece of any natural wood can be **split** in one direction and not in another (Fig. 1). You will have noticed this if you have chopped firewood or seen it being done (Fig. 2).

We say that wood has **grain**. This effects how it behaves and how we use it.

Grain direction

A piece of wood with the grain running across it is far weaker than the same-sized piece with grain running along its length. Fig. 3 shows another way of proving this. Which piece would your rather have as your chair leg?

The grain direction is very important when you are planning and making a project. Parts of the toy animal in Fig. 4 would snap off easily in use.

Holes and fixings

Holes, nails or screws too close together in line along the grain can also spell disaster (Fig. 5(a)). The bottom piece, (b) has the same number of holes but is less likely to split.

Planing

Planing the end grain of wood must be done in a special way (see p. 69, Fig. 4) to avoid disaster.

Fig. 1 **Grain:** wood is much weaker 'along the grain' than 'across the grain'.

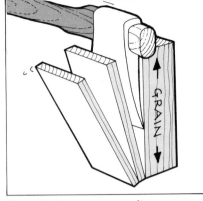

Fig. 2 **Grain:** we use wood's weakness along the grain when chopping firewood.

Fig. 3 **Grain direction:** 'short grain' breaks easily.

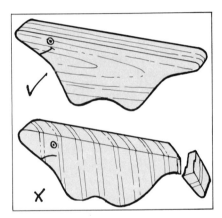

Fig. 4 **Grain direction:** this is important when planning your projects.

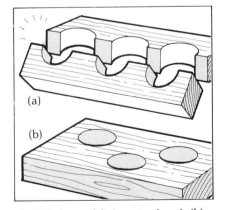

Fig. 5 **Holes and fixings:** tool rack (b) is stronger.

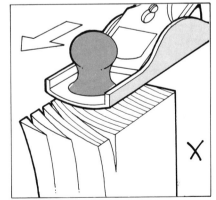

Fig. 6 **Planing:** there is a special way to plane the end grain.

1 *Copy the animal in Fig. 4 and show the grain direction. Draw heavy lines to show where else it would break easily.*
2 *Bend a match slowly and watch closely as it breaks. Write a sentence or more to describe what you see.*

Man-made boards — plywood and hardboard

You can split a piece of wood quite easily along the grain. Although this is useful when chopping firewood this weakness is usually a problem.

▋Plywood

People have overcome this problem by making **plywood.** This is made up of thin layers of wood called **veneers.** Each piece is glued to the next with the grains at *right angles* to each other (Fig. 1(a)). This makes it strong and stops it splitting.

Plywood is also less likely to **warp** or **twist** than real wood. Use **exterior** or **marine** plywood if your project will get wet.

Plywood even does its share for conservation as rare and expensive woods are only ever used for the layers that can be seen on the surface.

Plywood bends more easily one way than the other. Notice how it bends across the grain direction of the outside layers (Fig. 2). Plywood can be used to make curves because it is **flexible** as well as strong.

You can nail or screw close to the edge of plywood without it splitting (Figure 3). Use a saw with small teeth (like a **tenon saw**) to cut plywood, or the surface may chip.

Hardboard

This is rather like strong cardboard (Fig.4). Hardboard is not as strong as plywood but is quite a lot cheaper. This makes it useful for some larger projects. Most hardboard must be kept dry.

Pegboard

Pegboard is hardboard with regular rows of holes in it (Fig. 5).

Fig. 1 **Plywood:** this is made up of thin layers of wood with the grain directions running at right angles in each layer (a). This makes it strong and stops it splitting (b).

Fig. 2 **Plywood:** It bends easily *across* the grain direction of the outside layers

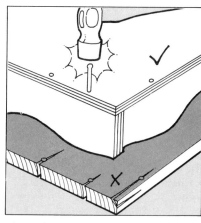

Fig. 3 **Plywood:** natural wood might split if nailed this close to the edge.

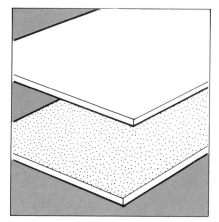

Fig. 4 **Hardboard:** one side is smooth, one side is textured.

Fig. 5 **Pegboard:** this piece has been used to make model levers.

---

1 *What is so good about plywood? List its good points.*
2 *Make a sample of plywood from scraps of veneer. What tests can you do on it?*

Basic things to know about metal

Metal is a very important material. We depend on it for many different things in our lives (Fig. 1). So you will certainly know what it looks and feels like.

▌ Sources of metal

The metal you use on projects was made from **ore** found in rocks. If used wastefully, some of the sources of ore will run out in the not-too-distant future. Metals can be **salvaged** and melted down to be used again.

▌ Rust

Some metals **rust**. Page 53 shows how to prevent this kind of waste.

▌ Alloys

Pure metals often have substances added to them to improve the way they behave; to make them **harder** for example. Sometimes two or more metals are mixed. We call this an **alloy. Brass** is one you might use. **Solder** (p. 93) is another useful alloy.

▌ Metal parts

Metal parts can be made in a number of ways. Although *you* will not use the methods shown in Fig. 2, items made like this will help you with your projects. You may see casting equipment in your CDT room. Chapter 4 shows ways *you* can work with metal.

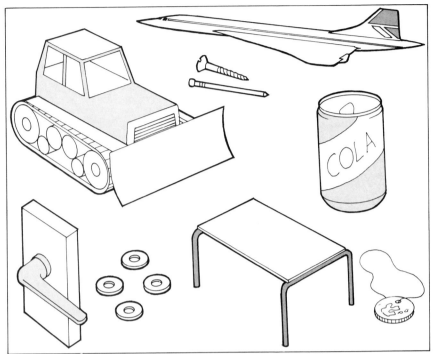

Fig. 1 We depend on metal for all sorts of things. What items do you use that include metal?

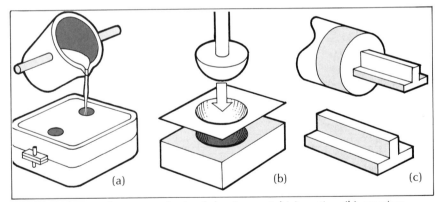

Fig. 2 **Metal parts:** factory methods of shaping metal (a) casting, (b) pressing, (c) extruding.

1 *Can you guess which processes in Fig. 2 were used to make the projects in Fig. 3? Can you give other examples of items made by* **casting, pressing** *or* **extruding?**
2 *List words you would use to describe metal to someone who had never seen or touched it.*

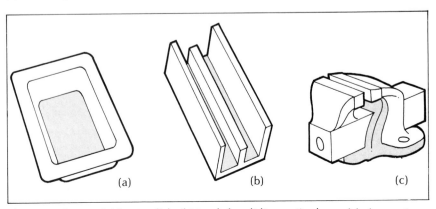

Fig. 3 **Metal parts:** (a) butter dish, (b) track for sliding patio doors, (c) vice parts.

How metals behave

Metals conduct heat
Metals feel cold because they conduct away your body's heat. So you can guess why there are no metal toilet seats! We use metal to conduct heat when cooking (Fig. 1(a)) but metal handles can be too hot (or too cold) for comfort (b).

Metals conduct electricity
Metal can be drawn out to make thin wire. We say it is a **ductile** material. Copper conducts electricity well and is used for most electrical wires. Aluminium foil can be used on some projects (p. 111).

NEVER use mains voltage on your projects.

█ Bending metal
We can bend and beat metal into shape, because metal is **malleable.** When we bend cold metal, the bend becomes stiffer and more **brittle.** This is called **work hardening.** If you try to bend and straighten metal too often, it may snap (Fig. 3).

Softening metal
Heating metal the right amount and letting it cool *slowly,* makes the bent part soft again (Fig. 4). (Ask your teacher's advice.) Heat can also be used to *harden* some metal and change it in other ways.

Fig. 1 **Metals conduct heat:** this can be a good or a bad thing.

Fig. 2 **Metal conducts electricity:** *never* use mains voltage on projects.

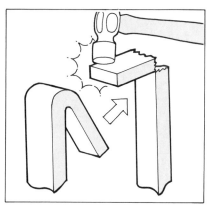

Fig. 3 **Bending metal:** this makes it stiff and brittle.

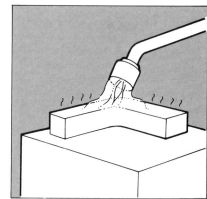

Fig. 4 **Softening metal:** heat the metal and let it cool slowly.

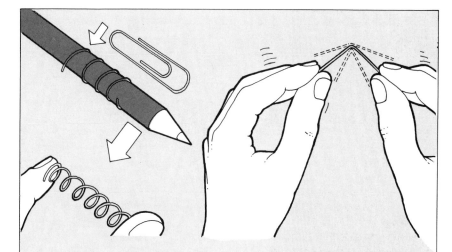

1 *Straighten a paperclip then wrap it round a pencil. Squeeze the coil and notice now it has* **work-hardened,** *making it springy.*
2 *Bend a straightened paperclip back and forth. How many bendings are needed to break it? Say why it breaks. What would happen if you were able to heat the bent paperclip and let it cool?*

Which metal — which shape?

Metal can be bought in many different shapes and sizes. Check that you can get the shape you want before finally deciding your design (Fig. 1).

Types of metal

We put metals into two groups:

Ferrous metals

These contain iron. Examples are steel and cast iron. These will rust or **corrode** unless protected.

Non-ferrous metals

These do not contain iron. Examples are aluminium and copper. These will not rust.

Mild steel

Steel is grey in colour. It rusts easily unless protected (p. 53). Car bodywork is usually made from steel (Fig. 2).

Tinplate

This is very shiny and silver in colour. It is made by coating thin sheets of steel with tin. Tin cans are made of this (Fig. 3). It is cheap but easily scratched, which allows the steel beneath to rust. It is easy to cut (p. 67) but *beware of sharp edges.*

Aluminium

This is silvery and may be shiny. It is fairly cheap, light and easy to work. It resists corrosion without being painted. This makes it good for outdoor or water projects (Fig. 4). It conducts heat and electricity well. You *cannot* solder it (p. 92).

Copper

This is reddish-brown in colour. It is quite tough and can be beaten into shape. It resists rusting and is a very good conductor of heat and electricity. Most electric wires are copper. It is expensive, so it is only used for small parts of projects (Fig. 5).

Look for these metals in use in your home or school. Make a list of products — for each metal.

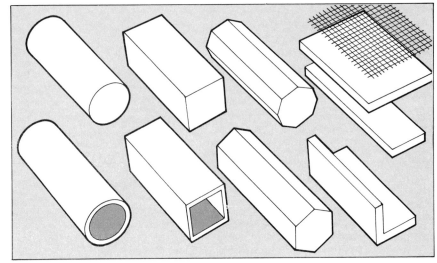

Fig. 1 Metal comes in a range of shapes and sizes.

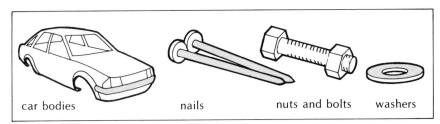

car bodies   nails   nuts and bolts   washers

Fig. 2 **Mild steel:** some of its uses.

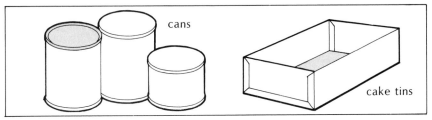

cans   cake tins

Fig. 3 **Tinplate:** some of its uses.

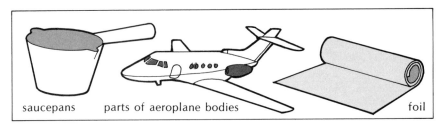

saucepans   parts of aeroplane bodies   foil

Fig. 4 **Aluminium:** some of its uses.

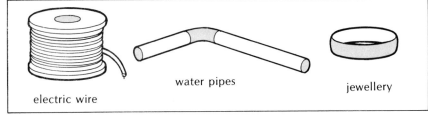

electric wire   water pipes   jewellery

Fig. 5 **Copper:** some of its uses.

Basic things to know about plastics

Compared with wood and metal, plastics are very new materials. They have been manufactured during the last forty years or so. There are many, many kinds of plastic and we use them for many very different jobs (Fig. 1). They can be made to behave in almost any way that is needed. You have probably come across plastics that are *hard, soft, brittle, flexible, transparent, coloured* and so on.

Most plastics are made from oil; a natural material which will run out quite soon if we use it wastefully. Getting rid of waste plastic without causing pollution can also be a problem. Perhaps we should stop thinking of plastic as such a disposable material.

■ Types of plastics
Plastics can be divided into two families:-
Thermoplastics
These plastics soften when you heat them.
Thermosets
These plastics burn away if you heat them.

■ Making items from plastic
Figure 2 shows how some everyday plastic items are made. Your school may have equipment to try out some of these processes on a small scale. Many other methods are used in the plastics industry. Elsewhere in this book you can find out how to work with plastic (pages 68, 78, 79)

(pages 68, 78, 79)

1 *Plastic is often used for items that were once made of wood or metal. Say why you think plastic buckets have mostly replaced metal ones.*
2 *Say how plastic bottles are better than glass ones.*
List as many uses as you can for empty plastic bottles.

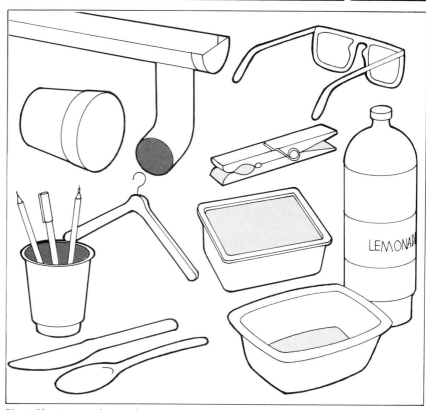

Fig. 1 Plastics can be made to suit an amazing variety of jobs and conditions.

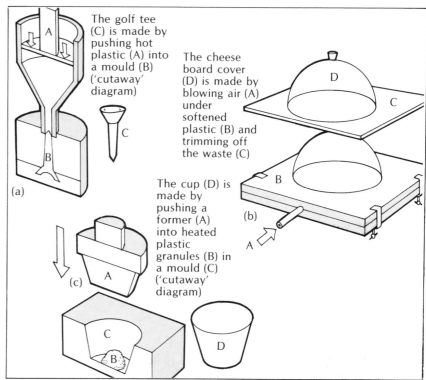

The golf tee (C) is made by pushing hot plastic (A) into a mould (B) ('cutaway' diagram)

The cheese board cover (D) is made by blowing air (A) under softened plastic (B) and trimming off the waste (C)

The cup (D) is made by pushing a former (A) into heated plastic granules (B) in a mould (C) ('cutaway' diagram)

Fig. 2 **Making items from plastic:** (a) Injection moulding   (b) blow moulding (c) compression moulding. Another method — vacuum forming — is described on page 79.

Some useful plastics — and how they behave

There is no room to describe all the different plastics, so here are three examples you may find useful on projects. Notice how different they are.

▍Acrylic

This can be clear or brightly coloured. It is normally **brittle** but softens when heated as it is a **thermoplastic.** *Light passes through it* so it is often used for shop and road signs (Fig. 1). The shiny surface *scratches* easily so keep the paper coating on as long as possible. Pages 68 and 78 show how to cut and shape acrylic. You can buy it in sheets, rods and tubes.

▍Expanded polystyrene

This is often used for packaging and ceiling tiles. It is very light and easily damaged. It floats and flies well (Fig. 2). It is a good heat **insulator** (keeps things warm or cold) and feels warm to touch. It can be cut with sharp tools but is rather crumbly.

▍Polythene

This can be cut easily from fruit drink and other household containers after you have washed them well. Polythene bags are useful for sails or kites (Fig 3). It is very flexible but can become brittle if exposed to the sun for a long time. It feels slippery and is good for cutting down **friction** when you want things to turn or slide.

> **1** *Draw a sign that could be made from acrylic and lit up. What would happen if a bulb was put too close?*
> **2** *Choose one of the special things about expanded polystyrene and draw a project that makes the most of this.*
> **3** *Use drawings to show how you would cut the largest possible sheet from a five litre polythene container (Fig. 3).*

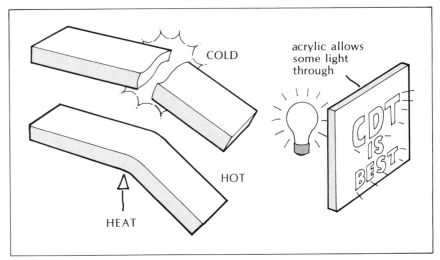
Fig. 1 **Acrylic:** how it behaves.

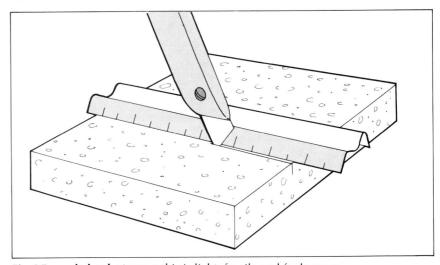
Fig. 2 **Expanded polystyrene:** this is light, fragile and feels warm.

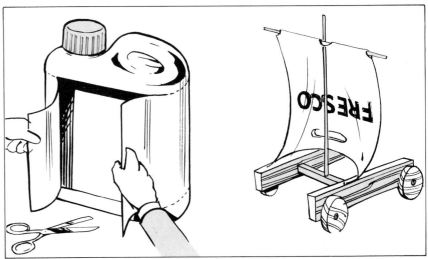
Fig. 3 **Polythene:** this has lots of uses and can be obtained free from bags and containers.

Smoothing materials with abrasives

An **abrasive** is something that wears away a softer material. Use abrasives to get your projects nice and smooth before painting, varnishing or polishing. The roughest are used first. These are followed by smoother and smoother ones for a really good finish.

Smoothing wood

Use **glasspaper** on wood. This is normally wrapped around a cork block (Fig. 1). Use a dowel rod when sanding curves. Always use glasspaper *along* the grain unless the work will be painted.

Figure 2 shows how to divide glasspaper and other abrasive sheets.

Smoothing metal

For steel, use the different grades of **emery** cloth or emery paper. Oil may be added for a smooth finish (Fig. 3).

On copper, brass and aluminium emery paper can be followed by **pumice powder paste** put on with a nail brush (Fig. 4(a)). For an even better finish rub along scratches with a **Water of Ayr stone** (Fig. 4(b)).

Smoothing acrylic (perspex)

Edges that have been filed and scraped (p. 68) can be polished with **silicon carbide paper** which is used wet. The surfaces can be polished with **chrome cleaner** or toothpaste, which is a gentle abrasive.

A buffing wheel can be used for polishing metal. Acrylic can also be polished this way but it must *not* be allowed to get hot. Ask your teacher to show you a safe method.

If a piece of wood was very rough, why would you use a plane to smooth it before using glasspaper?

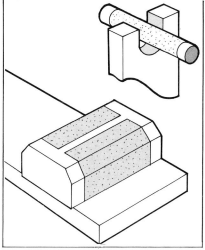

Fig. 1 Sanding wood with the help of a cork block and wooden dowel rod.

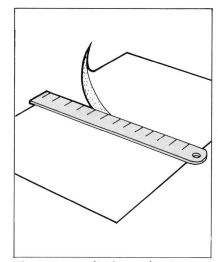

Fig. 2 How to divide up abrasive sheets.

Fig. 3 Emery cloth used on metal. Add oil when larger scratches are gone.

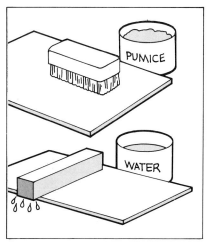

Fig. 4 Using pumice powder paste followed by Water of Ayr stone.

Fig. 5 Smoothing acrylic.

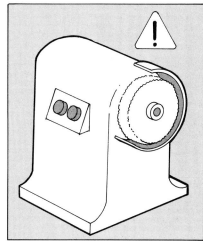

Fig. 6 A buffing wheel.

Use **surface finishes** to protect materials and improve the way they look. Choosing the right one for your project is an important part of designing and making. Shops display many different types and colours. Here are some you will find useful. Always follow the maker's instructions and keep them off your skin and clothes. (See page 54 on using a brush.)

Varnish (for wood, copper, brass)
Gloss or matt varnish gives a tough, clear finish that will wipe clean (Fig. 1). Special kinds are good for water and outdoor projects. Use a clean brush. More than one coat is best. Give it plenty of time to dry.

To smooth varnish, rub lightly with fine wire wool. Wax and then polish to improve the feel (Fig. 2).

Cooking oil (for wood)
This is good for salad servers and other wooden projects that will be used with food. It shows off the colour and grain. Wipe on with a clean cloth, allow to soak in, then wipe dry.

Wood dye and stain
This changes the colour of wood but the grain can still be seen (Fig. 4). End grain soaks up more and goes darker. Test on scrap pieces. Keep it off your hands.

Paint (for wood, metal, plastics)
There are several different kinds, so always read the tin. **Emulsion** paints are good for wood indoors when a shine is not needed. They dry fast and brushes and hands can be cleaned in water. Other paints need plenty of time to dry. Three coats of paint give the best finish (Fig. 5).

Wood preservers
Use these on outdoor wooden projects only. (Fig. 6). Be well protected as some kinds can be nasty. Avoid splashes; wear goggles just in case.

What finish would you choose for: a tray, spatula, wind powered model? Add others.

Fig. 1 **Varnish:** use more than one coat to give the best results.

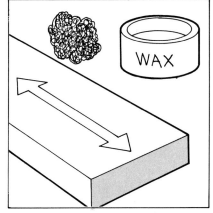
Fig. 2 **Varnish:** smooth it with wire wool and wax.

Fig. 3 **Cooking oil:** this is safe for work used with food.

Fig. 4 **Wood dye and stain:** stain gives colour but lets the grain show.

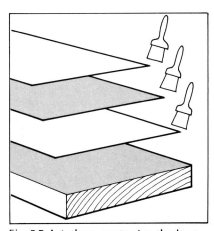
Fig. 5 **Paint:** three coats give the best finish.

Fig. 6 **Wood preservers:** useful for some outdoor projects.

How to use and care for a paintbrush

How can you do a good job and avoid making a mess of your work, the CDT room and yourself?

1 Wear an apron and roll up your sleeves. Tie back long hair. Wear disposable gloves or plastic bags on your hands, this is easier than cleaning them (Fig. 1)!

2 Cover the bench with newspaper.

3 Work out the best way to hold the work before you start (Fig. 2).

4 Find out where to put work while it dries. The best place is away from dust — and fingers!

5 It is sometimes easier to paint parts before putting them together.

▌Opening the tin
Hold the tin firmly as shown in Fig. 3. This keeps your hand out of danger when you ease off the lid with a screwdriver. Do *not* use a chisel or you could have a bad accident.

▌Using the brush
Hold it like a pen. Dip less than half the bristle in. Scrape extra paint or varnish back into the tin to avoid drips.

Brush towards edges as shown in Fig. 4 or tears will run down the sides of the work. Try for a thin, even coat.

▌Cleaning the brush
The brush *must* be well cleaned. Scrape both sides onto newspaper (Fig. 5). Fold this up and put it in a bin.

You can wash off emulsion paint under the tap. For other paint and varnish use **white spirit** or turpentine substitute (Fig. 6). Do this well away from flames or sparks in a well-ventilated place. Finally, wash the brush with soap and water.

Fig. 1 Get yourself ready before you start.

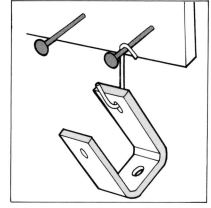

Fig. 2 Decide how to hold the work.

Fig. 3 **Opening the tin:** hold it as shown.

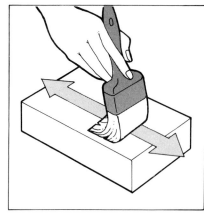

Fig. 4 **Using the brush:** use only the end.

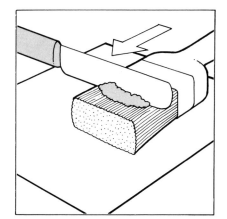

Fig. 5 **Cleaning the brush:** scrape off excess paint onto newspaper.

Fig. 6 **Cleaning the brush:** use white spirit or turps substitute for all paints except emulsion.

Design a helpful poster to go near your painting area.

We have looked at some important raw materials but there are many extras that can be bought to add a finishing touch. Use your imagination to find new uses for everyday products. Here are a few examples to set you thinking.

Googley eyes
These add fun and personality to the simplest shape (Fig. 1). Buy them from craft shops and fix well with epoxy resin (p. 00).

Coloured tapes
These are quick and easy ways to add colour. But don't overdo it! Use two different ones to make stripes or cut out arrows and other shapes. Use them to colour code things like switches e.g. green for OFF red for ON. Buy them from DIY and cycle shops.

Pipe insulation
This is light, soft and flexible, but tough. It gives a warm, non-slip grip and can be wiped clean. Short pieces make good tyres. Could you use it to make a switch that has to be squeezed? It is easy to cut with a sharp knife or a fine-toothed saw. Buy it from a DIY shop.

Rub-on letters and numbers
Use these to decorate or communicate (Fig. 4). They are good for scores on games. They can be covered with clear tape for protection.

Useful stickers or **decals** also come with video tapes and model kits.

> Test your imagination! List as many uses as you can for
> (a) a metre of string:
> (b) a house brick.

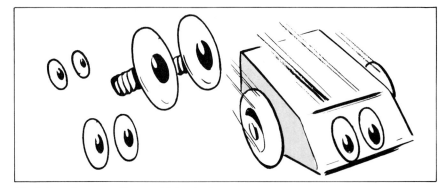

Fig. 1 **Googley eyes:** these add fun to toys.

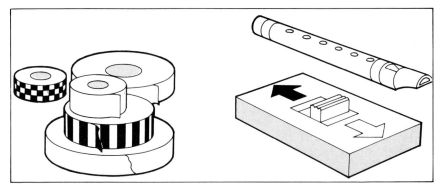

Fig. 2 **Coloured tapes:** these give colour that decorates and communicates.

Fig. 3 **Pipe insulation:** this is useful for tyres, planes and handles. Can you think of other uses?

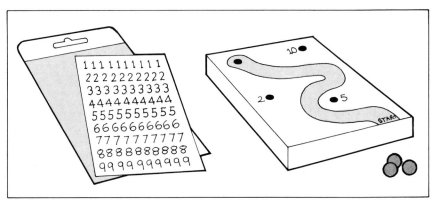

Fig. 4 **Rub-on letters and numbers:** these give a neat finish.

Getting parts for projects — free!

We live in a very wasteful society where thousands of useful things are thrown away every day. People may be just bored with them or want a newer version. Even when something is worn out it still has *lots* of valuable parts that you can use on projects. This is a very good idea because:

- it saves you a lot of money
- it gives you parts and materials you might not have thought of
- it saves our planet's materials and energy and reduces pollution.

Whatever you need, someone somewhere is probably throwing it away!

▌ Recycling

Recycling or **salvaging** will help you learn how things work, and how they are put together. You might even be able to mend something and give it a good home.

Do *not* try this with electrical goods unless they are battery powered. An unplugged TV set can still be dangerous, so leave them alone.

Always ask the owner before recycling something!

You could advertise in your school for broken and unwanted items. Jumble sales are another good place to find things. Figure 2 shows some of the useful parts that can be found. More ideas will be found elsewhere in this book.

Design a poster asking people to bring in unwanted items. Explain why you need them and why recycling is such a good idea.

Fig. 1 Use salvaged parts for projects and let people know what you need.

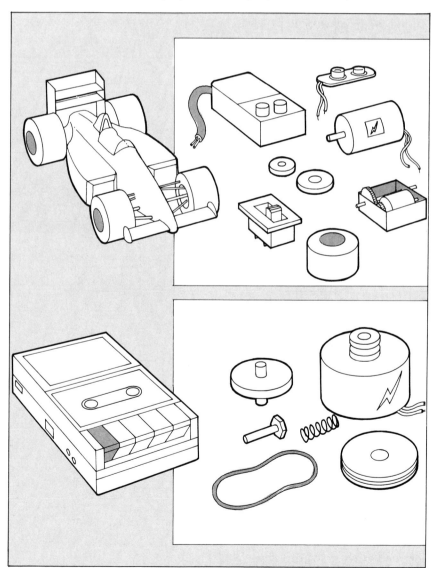

Fig. 2 Unwanted household goods are a useful source of parts for projects.

More free materials

Plastic bottles

Plastic bottle bottoms (Fig. 1) can be slotted together to make lightweight wheels. You may need help to pull off the bottoms. Bottles can be used as floats, mini greenhouses and many other things.

Cut the plastic bottles up to get clear plastic for windscreens and so on.

Aerosol caps

Aerosol caps (Fig. 2) can be screwed to or bolted to desk tidies, storage racks and similar projects. These are good for holding paper clips and other small things. Another use is to hold ping-pong balls on a siege engine project.

Flex insulation

Electric flex **insulation** or **sleeving** (Fig. 3) can be pushed over metal flexible joints or to stop wheels coming off axles. Take out the wire inside before cutting flex into pieces with a knife.

Syringe cases

Syringe cases come with syringes used for hydraulic or pneumatic projects (p. 118). Ask your teacher for them. Fig. 4 shows some possible uses.

Choose some easy-to-get, throw-away item and use drawings and notes to suggest uses for it.

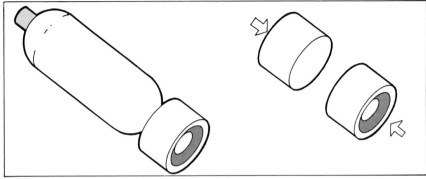

Fig. 1. **Plastic bottles:** these have many uses.

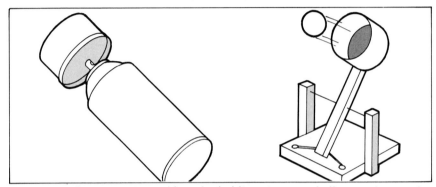

Fig. 2 **Aerosol caps:** one is used here for holding ping pong balls on a siege engine project.

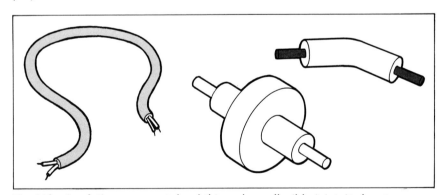

Fig. 3 **Flex insulation:** on a metal rod this makes a flexible joint; it also stops wheels coming off axles.

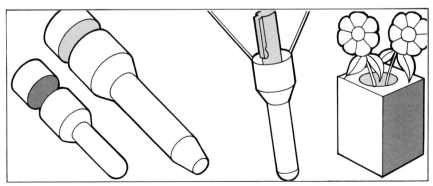

Fig. 4 **Syringe cases**

Free materials — get them before they reach the dustbin!

We use and waste a lot of 'disposable' things everyday. With a little imagination you can give them a second life by using them on projects. Remember that those shown on this page are only examples. Look for other throw-away things that you can put to good use. The things shown here would be difficult for you to make; luckily there's no need to.

Old rubber inner tubes can be sliced up to make *rubber bands, tyres* and *belts* for pulleys (p. 106). They are good for making non-slip surfaces.

Cotton reels make good *wheels* and *pulleys*. Cut the outside off some kinds to make a small *turbine* or paddle wheel.

Drink cans can be made into *wheels* or filled with sand, or concrete to make *weights*. Cut them up to get very thin metal; but watch out for sharp edges. Another use is shown on p. 117.

Plastic containers come in many shapes and sizes, they have lots of uses. They are good for *storing* small parts. Some will make *floats* or *tubes* or you could cut them up and use the plastic. Avoid ones that have held nasty chemicals.

Detergent bottles make good *floats, wheels, pneumatic pumps* (p. 119) or *skittles* for a target game. Cut the top off to make a funnel or part for a wind-powered project.

Cassette cases make good *control boxes* and *battery holders* for electric powered projects. They are even better if painted matt black. Drill carefully to avoid cracking.

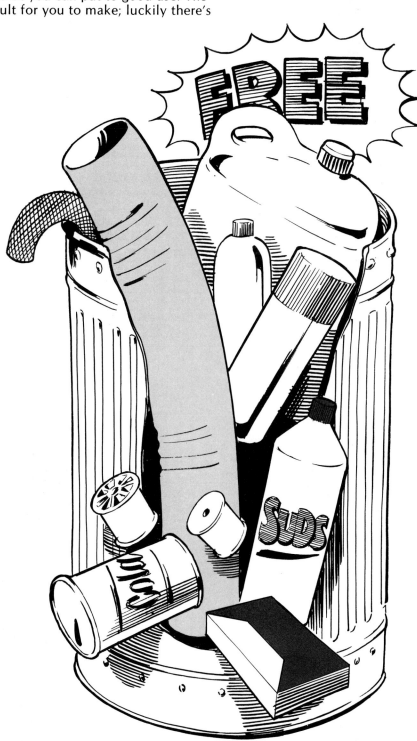

Use drawings and notes to show even more ways of re-using some of the things shown here.

Question 1

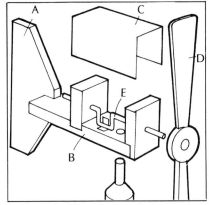

Question 2

Question 3

1 You have been beamed up by friendly aliens who want to know more about Earth before they risk landing. They are very interested in the materials we use, what they are like and what we use them for.

1.1 Tell them as much as you can about:

(a) wood; (b) metal;

(c) plastic.

You can't show them any examples but you can use drawings when it helps.

1.2 Tell the aliens about the need to avoid wasting materials on your planet. Describe some ways of saving or re-using materials.

1.3 In return for your help they show you a strange material that is important on their planet. Say what it is called, what it is like and how it behaves.

2 Here is a drawing of a wind-powered machine that clicks as it turns. The right materials must be used if it is to work well and go on working.

2.1 Say what *you* would use to make the labelled parts. You may be able to give more than one answer, e.g. (a) tinplate or (b) acrylic.

2.2 Choose *one* of the parts and name at least one material it should *not* be made from. Give your reasons.

2.3 This project will be outside in all weathers. Some of the materials you have chosen will need protection. Describe how you would preserve them and make them look attractive.

2.4 Draw all the *wooden* parts and show the grain direction.

3 You are trapped on a desert island. Washed up on the beaches are plastic bottles, tins, polystyrene packaging, a pullover made from strong nylon wool and other thrown-away objects.

3.1 How would you use these items to help you survive and make life more comfortable? Use drawings to explain your ideas. Think about:

(a) collecting and storing food and water;

(b) shelter from storms;

(c) attracting rescuers and escape plans.

3.2 You would need to work with many different materials, both natural and man made. What *five* tools would you wish for most? Give reasons.

3.3 You need to cross a deep crevice in the rock. Two planks have been washed ashore. They are long enough to bridge the gap but not strong enough if just laid across as shown. Use drawings to explain how you could use the planks to get you across.

How do I make it?

This machine cut the edges of this book. It can cut an average of 2500 books per hour. There are many safety features to avoid accidents. You will be using smaller machines in CDT and must always be aware of safety rules.

Making your projects — safely

How is a CDT room like a jungle?

Answer: Both are interesting and exciting places but both can be dangerous if you are silly or don't know what you are doing. In both places you need good information and an expert guide. Your teacher and this book will show you how to work safely. Consult them if in doubt and report anything spilled or damaged.

How to avoid accidents

Accidents can change your whole life in a moment. Here are some ways of preventing them:

You need protection!

Being properly dressed is important, in the jungle and in CDT (Fig. 2).

● Wear an apron and roll up your sleeves.

● Tie back long hair, tuck in ties and other loose clothing.

● Wear a visor or goggles when using machinery.

● Use gloves when necessary.

● Wear strong shoes.

More haste, less safety!

Like travellers in the jungle, you depend on one another for your safety. One person rushing down a room puts everyone else at risk (Fig. 3).

● Never rush or run in a CDT room and take care when carrying tools.

● Concentrate on what you are doing.

● Don't talk to someone using a machine or hot materials. This includes your teacher.

Hold it!

● Hold all work securely and in the correct way (Fig. 4).

● Don't have work sticking out into gangways.

● Never cut *towards* yourself.

If in doubt, ask

● Never use equipment without permission.

● Know how to switch equipment OFF and where all STOP buttons are. (Fig. 5).

Fig 1 In the jungle and the CDT room, your safety depends on knowing how and taking care.

Design safety posters and signs for your CDT room. Use symbols to help (p. 33).

Fig. 2 **You need protection:** dress properly.

Fig. 3 **More haste, less safety!:** never rush about.

Fig. 4 **Hold it!:** hold work properly.

Fig. 5 **If in doubt, ask:** know where STOP buttons are.

Marking lines at an angle from a straight edge

Lines at 90° to a straight edge

Use a **marking knife** when the line is to show where to cut. Use a sharp, soft pencil for lines you will need to rub out later.

Marking wood

1 Put the knife or pencil point where you want the line.

2 Slide the square up to the knife or pencil and squeeze it against the wood (Fig. 1).

3 Hold your marking knife like a pencil. Make sure your fingertips are out of the way, then mark the line firmly.

Never drop or bang a square or you may spoil its accuracy.

Marking metal

A **scriber** is the usual tool for marking on metal. A pencil can be used on copper, aluminium or tinplate when you don't want to scratch the surface.

1 Wipe off any oil on the metal, then paint it with marking blue. This will dry quickly and make scriber lines easier to see.

2 Press the square firmly against a straight edge (Fig. 2).

3 Hold the scriber like a pen and mark the line firmly.

Never hit the scriber with a hammer.

Lines at 45° to a straight edge

Use a **mitre-square** squeezed against a straight edge. These are often used to mark corner joints like those found on picture frames (Fig. 3).

Lines at any angle

Adjust the **sliding bevel** (Fig. 4) to the angle you want. You may need a screwdriver.

Marking plastic

Use a fine-line marker pen with any of the tools shown on this page. For acrylic see p. 68.

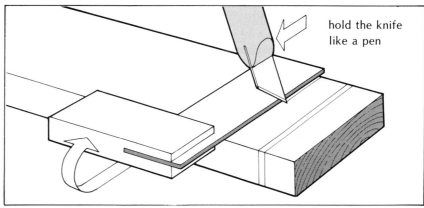

hold the knife like a pen

Fig. 1 Squeeze squares tight against the work. The sawing board can help.

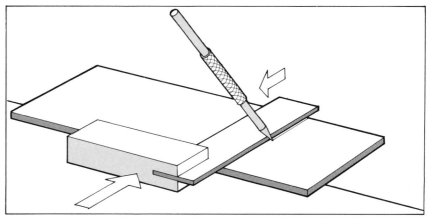

Fig. 2 **Marking metal**: this material should overhang the bench a little.

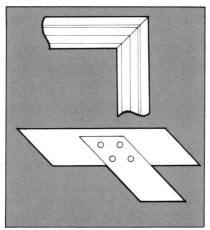

Fig. 3 **Lines at 45° to a straight edge**: use a mitre-square.

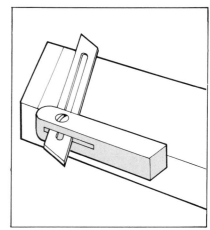

Fig. 4 **Lines at any angle**: use a sliding bevel.

The tools mentioned above should not be pressed against a crooked edge. Explain why. Start by drawing a very crooked edge.

Marking lines parallel to an edge

Lines parallel to an edge are useful when you want to:

- cut strips off
- mark rows of holes
- cut material a certain width
- mark out joints and slots.

▎Wood

Don't use the **marking gauge** *across* the grain as this tears the wood. (See page 45.)

1 Loosen the screw and set the gauge to the distance you want (Fig. 1(a)).

2 Hold the wood in a vice.

3 With the **spur** pointing towards you, push the gauge *away* to mark the line. The **stock** and the corner of the **stem** should rub against the wood.

▎Metal

1 Set the **odd-leg-callipers** to the size you want (Fig. 2(a)).

2 Lean the tool away from you slightly and mark the line. Thin metal should hang over the bench edge a little. Can you see why?

When you don't want to scratch the surface (of acrylic or tinplate for example) mark the line this way (Fig 2). Measure across each end and join the marks with a ruler and a soft pencil or felt pen.

Using a marking gauge on metal could damage the tool. Say how.

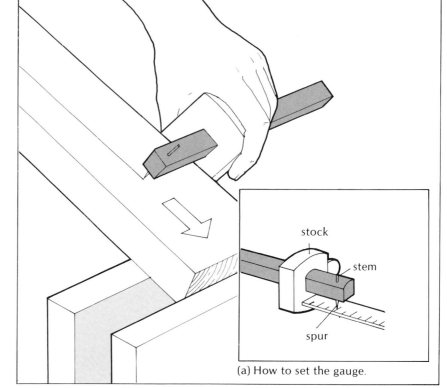

stock

stem

spur

(a) How to set the gauge.

Fig. 1 **Wood:** using a marking gauge.

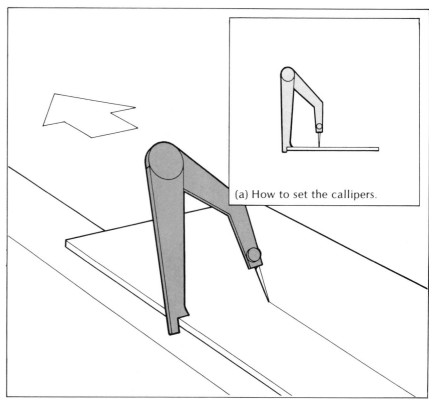

(a) How to set the callipers.

Fig. 2 **Metal:** using odd-leg callipers.

Sawing pieces off wood

Sawing is a quick way of removing unwanted wood, making joints or cutting pieces from a length. You will use the **tenon saw** most (Fig. 1).

When cutting *across* the grain use it with a **bench hook** as shown.

Here are some hints:

1 Hold the saw as shown in Fig. 1 with your first finger pointed.

2 Use your thumb against the side of the blade, not the teeth, and pull the saw backwards to start it in the right place.

3 Use the whole blade and do not force the saw.

4 Keep wood-saw teeth away from metal.

▌Plywood sheet
The tenon saw's small teeth make it good for cutting thin sheet without splitting. Hold small sheets on the bench hook. Large pieces should be supported on trestles or stools (Fig. 2).

▌Strips off a wide board
Cutting along the grain is called **ripping**. A handsaw is used. Cut between two marking gauge lines (p. 63). Feed the work up out of the vice as it is cut (Fig. 3).

▌Handles and slots
The **coping saw** is usually used to cut curves (see p. 71) but it can be used for straight lines when other saws can't reach. Remove the blade (Fig. 4) and pass it through a hole in your work. Refix the blade and cut the slot (Fig. 5). The blade can cut at any angle but the blade must *not* be twisted.

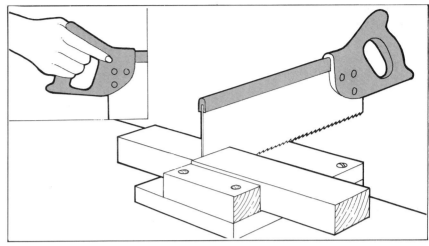

Fig. 1 Using a tenon saw and bench hook. Always cut just to the waste side of a line, never *on* the line.

Fig. 2 **Plywood sheet:** cutting a large piece of thin sheet.

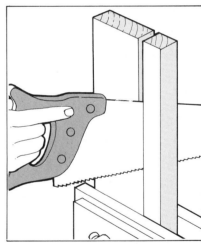

Fig. 3 **Strips off a wide board:** use a handsaw.

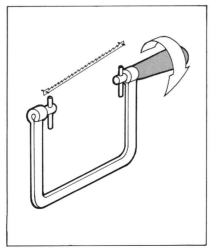

Fig. 4 **Handles and slots:** how to remove the coping saw blade.

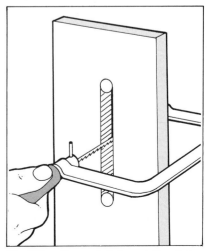

Fig. 5 **Handles and slots:** cut the slot as shown.

Cutting several pieces the same — jigs

Marking out lots of pieces the same can be boring. A simple **jig** means you don't have to do this. Jigs can also help if a number of people need a piece exactly the same. Here are some ideas to start you thinking. You may be able to design other jigs to suit your projects.

▌ **Cutting pieces the same length**
This jig (Fig. 1) is easily screwed and glued together (see pages 84, 87). It is used to cut wooden blocks and dowel.

▌ **Cutting short pieces of dowel**
This is quick to make and a time-saver when you want lots of pieces of dowel the same. Push the dowel through the hole until it is level with the end of the block; then cut (Fig. 2). Rest your free hand on the dowel to stop it rolling as you saw.

▌ **Cutting corners the same**
Shape a piece of wood to match the corners you want. This is cramped onto each piece of work and used to guide a chisel (Fig. 3). Cut a little at a time.

▌ **Drilling in the same place**
Line the jig up with edges of the work and you can drill holes in the same position on each piece (Fig. 4).

▌ **Drilling holes at the same angle**
Take a block and drill a hole at the angle you want (Fig. 5). Cramp it to the work to make holes at the same angle each time.

When is it worth making a jig instead of marking and cutting separate pieces?
What are the good things about using a jig?

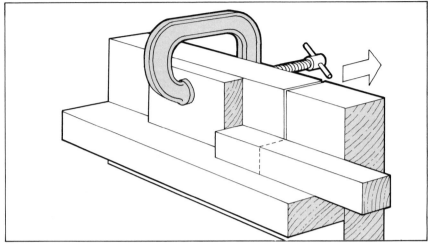

Fig. 1 **Cutting pieces the same length:** hold the jig in a vice.

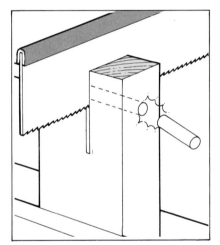

Fig. 2 **Cutting short pieces of dowel:** line up the end of the dowel with the end of the block.

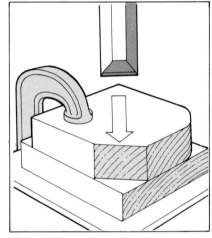

Fig. 3 **Cutting corners the same:** shape a piece of wood to match the corners you want.

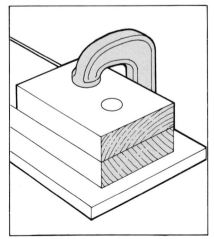

Fig. 4 **Drilling in the same place:** line up the jig with the edges of the work.

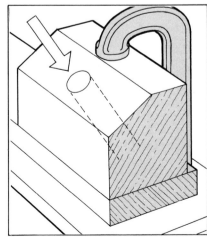

Fig. 5 **Drilling holes at the same angle:** drill a hole at the required angle to make your jig.

Sawing pieces off metal

Metal that is too thick to be cut with **tinsnips** (p. 67) should be cut with a **hacksaw** (Fig. 1). A **junior hacksaw** is useful for thinner metal and lighter tasks. Use it to cut wooden dowel without splintering. Hacksaws will cut most materials including acrylic. Your teacher will provide a suitable blade.

Using a hacksaw
Saw steadily using the whole blade. Cut close to the vice. Protect your work with soft metal or wood to cover the vice jaws.

Changing the blade
Blades that are worn out or damaged must be replaced (Fig. 2). Undo the wing nut at the front; a rag will make it more comfortable to grip. Fit the new blade with its *teeth pointing forward*. Tighten the wing nut again. Slots can be cut by fitting two or more blades at the same time.

Push a junior hacksaw against the bench to remove or fit a blade (Fig. 3).

Sawing long pieces
To stop the frame getting in the way you can take the blade out and refit it turned through 90° (Fig. 4). Feed the work up as it is cut.

Sawing complicated shapes
An **abrafile** is good for cutting shapes in metal and hard plastics. Figure 5 shows it close up and how it is fitted to the frame.

Draw the two junior hacksaws in Fig. 3. Label the one you would prefer to use and say why. Say which you think costs most.

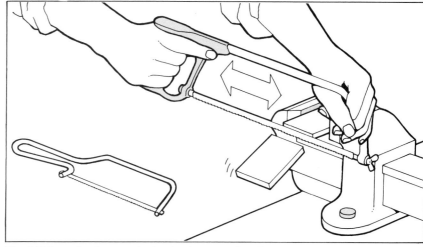

Fig. 1 **Using a hacksaw:** a junior hacksaw is also shown.

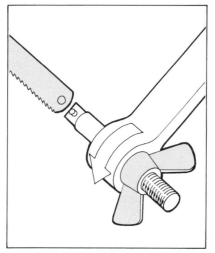

Fig. 2 **Changing a blade:** undo the wing nut.

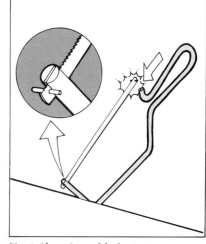

Fig. 3 **Changing a blade:** junior hacksaw.

Fig. 4 **Sawing long pieces:** feed the work up as it is cut.

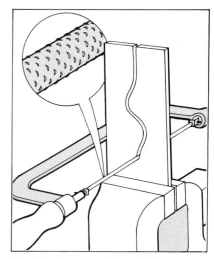

Fig. 5 **Sawing complicated shapes:** use an abrafile.

Tinsnips

Thin sheet metal can be cut with **tinsnips** just as card is cut with scissors. Once cut the sheet metal can be folded and joined (p. 36) into 3D objects like the digger scoop in Fig. 1. A card model should be made first. Some other ideas are also shown.

Sheet metal has *very sharp* edges, especially after being cut with snips. Handle it with care — strong gloves are a good idea. Edges may be folded over to make them safer and stronger (p. 77).

Straight cuts

Use straight snips for straight lines and convex shapes that don't curve too much (Fig. 2). Don't close the blades right up or you will get a ragged line and wrinkle the edge of your work.

You can hold one handle in the metalwork vice when extra pressure is needed, but don't try to cut metal that is too thick.

Circles and curves

Curved snips can be used for all sorts of curves. Choose a smaller pair for small work and tight curves. As with straight snips, keep them upright and don't close them all the way.

Multi-purpose snips

Use these multi-purpose snips on thin metal (Fig. 5). They will cut a variety of light materials including paper and fabric. They are ideal for making models and other light work.

1 What happens if you close the snips right up as you cut? Draw and label your answer.
2 Which snips would you use to cut aluminium foil? Draw your answer.

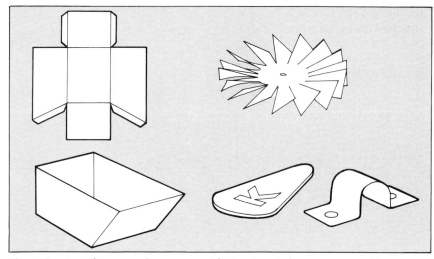

Fig. 1 **Tinsnips:** Sheet metal parts cut with tinsnips. A digger scoop and its flattened form: a **development**.

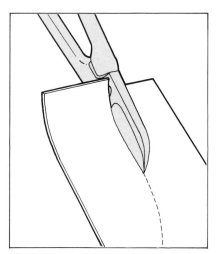

Fig. 2 **Straight cuts:** cutting a straight line and a convex curve.

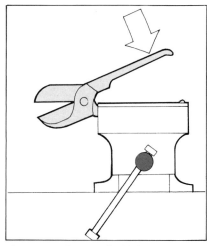

Fig. 3 **Straight cuts:** hold the handle in a vice for extra pressure.

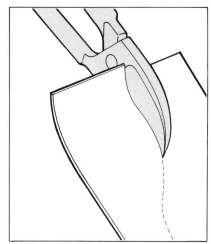

Fig. 4 **Circles and curves:** use curved snips.

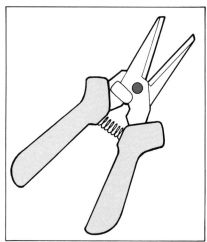

Fig. 5 **Multi-purpose snips:** suitable for light work only.

Cutting acrylic sheet and smoothing its edges

Acrylic is a brittle material. This is useful when we want to cut pieces from a strip.

▐ Scoring acrylic

1 Remove the top piece of protecting paper.

2 Score a deep line using a square and scoring tool. The back of a marking knife works well if you have no special scoring tool (Fig. 1).

▐ Breaking the acrylic

Line your score mark up with the edge of the bench (Fig. 2). Hold the sheet down firmly and press as shown.

▐ Smoothing the edge

Make a scraper from an old hacksaw blade. The edge without teeth is used (Fig. 3). Tape each end to protect your hands. Sharpen as shown on a piece of emery cloth. You can now smooth the acrylic and remove sharp edges too by tilting your scraper.

▐ Cutting curves

Mark the curve with felt pen or use PVA wood glue to stick on a paper pattern.
Protect the work from scratching by padding the vice with card. Cut with an abrafile held in a hacksaw frame (Fig. 4).
Always cut close to the vice, feeding the acrylic up as it is cut (Fig. 5). Otherwise it may break.

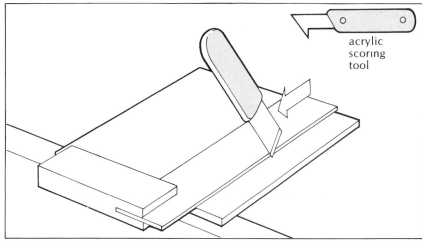

acrylic scoring tool

Fig. 1 **Scoring acrylic:** a marking knife used back-to-front can be kept for this job. Overhang the bench a little to avoid marking it.

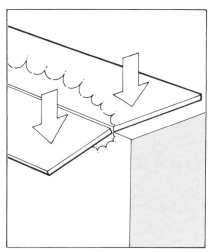

Fig. 2 **Breaking acrylic:** along the score line.

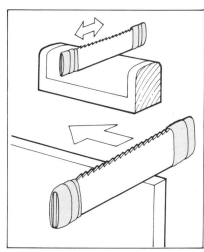

Fig. 3 **Smoothing the edge:** use an old hacksaw blade.

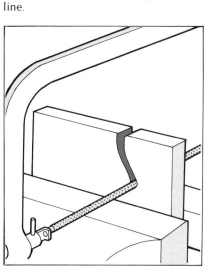

Fig. 4 **Cutting curves:** use an abrafile.

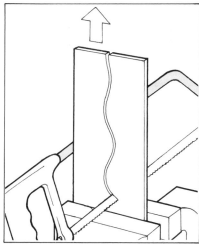

Fig. 5 **Cutting curves:** feed up the acrylic as you cut.

A sharp and properly adjusted plane can shape wood accurately leaving it smooth and clean. Here's how to look after your plane:

● Take care not to plane into nails or other metal.

● Leave the plane on its side when not in use and be sure not to drop it.

● Never poke anything into the **mouth** of your plane.

● Show it to your teacher if it won't work properly.

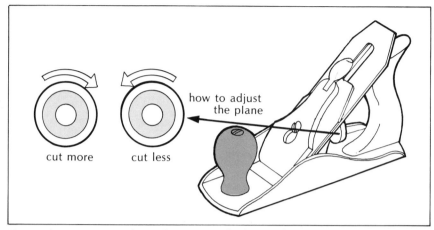

Fig. 1 Adjusting a **smoothing plane** to cut thicker or thinner shavings.

Making wood thinner, smoother and flatter

Narrow work can be held in the vice. Hold wide pieces as shown in Fig. 2. Gauge lines help with accurate work (p. 63). The mark shows it is flat. *Do not plane the surface of plywood.*

Making right-angled edges or 'planing wood square'

This is important when doing accurate work like making joints. Plane to a gauge line (see p. 63). Use a rule to see if your wood is straight and a try-square (Fig. 3 inset) to see if it is **square.** The mark in Fig. 3 is used to show it is square.

Planing the end of wood

This makes it split badly unless you hold some spare wood tightly behind. Planing the corner off your spare wood stops it splitting (Fig. 4). A knife line scored round the work helps.

Rounding off edges

This can be important for safety and comfort. The plane should only cut thin shavings and be tilted to a different angle on each stroke (Fig. 5). Finish with a file and glasspaper.

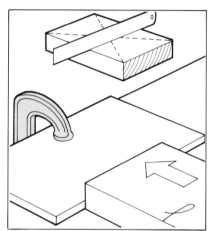

Fig. 2 The mark shows the work is straight and flat.

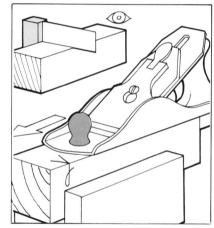

Fig. 3 **Making right-angled edges:** the mark shows it is square.

Fig. 4 **Planing the end of wood:** hold spare wood behind to stop splitting.

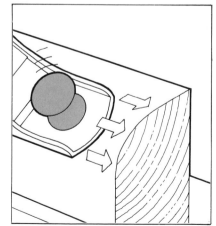

Fig. 5 **Rounding off edges:** cut thin shavings only.

Design a poster that will remind people how to care for a plane.

Files are used for shaping and smoothing metal and other materials. The **hacksaw** (p. 66) removes metal quickly but leaves a ragged edge. Use a file to smooth the edge exactly to a line.

Files are hard but brittle so:

● Never bang them together or use them as levers.

● Keep them away from oil or grease.

● It is dangerous to use a file without a handle.

How to file

After marking out your metal (pp. 62, 63) put it low in the vice using **soft vice jaws** or wood to protect it. To remove a lot of metal hold the file as shown in Fig. 2. For a lighter more delicate cut use only the thumb and first finger of your front hand. Always lift the file off the work when you bring it back for another stroke.

To file straight keep your wrist firm and the file in a straight line with your elbow. Check it with a try-square (Fig. 3). When filing curves bend your wrist to follow the line.

Cleaning your file

Files sometimes get clogged up and scratch the work. Rest the end of the file on the bench and brush along the teeth with a special wire brush called a **file card** (Fig. 4). A little chalk rubbed on the file helps keep the teeth clean.

Removing file marks

To leave a fine finish first clean the rule and rub it with chalk. Hold it with both hands and move it across the work as shown in Fig. 5. This is called **drawfiling.** For an even better surface wrap emery cloth round the file.

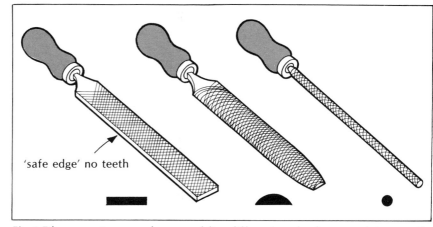

'safe edge' no teeth

Fig. 1 Files come in many shapes and five different grades from rough to smooth. Why do you think this is?

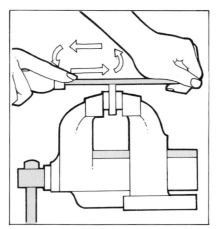

Fig. 2 **How to file:** lift the file on the return stroke.

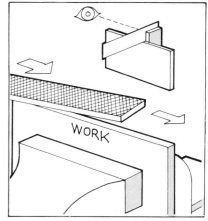

Fig. 3 **How to file:** keep the file in a straight line with your elbow.

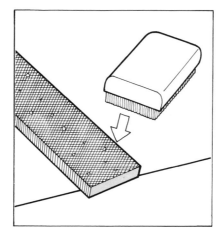

Fig. 4 **Cleaning your file:** use a file brush.

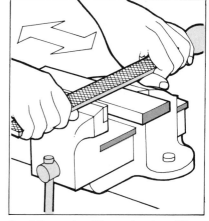

Fig. 5 **Removing file marks:** drawfiling for a fine finish.

Explain why (a) files should never be banged together (b) files should be kept away from oil and grease.

Curves may be used to make a project safer or more attractive.

▮ Thin timber and plywood

Use a **coping saw** (Fig. 1). Check that the blade is not twisted before you start and remember that it is easily broken. Don't cut too close to the line as you will need to **finish** the curve with other tools (see below).

▮ Solid timber

Using a **tenon saw,** make cuts towards the line but not touching it. A **mallet** and **chisel** used as shown will remove the unwanted wood (Fig. 2). Leave some wood to be smoothed with other tools (see below).

▮ Rounding off sharp corners

This can be done with a **file** or **surform** (see below) but it is quicker to use a chisel first. Use a G-cramp to hold the work onto some waste wood. Hold the chisel as shown and cut a little at a time (Fig. 3). Keep your elbow close to your body. Smooth with a **spokeshave.** (See Fig. 6).

▮ Rounding a long edge

Set your plane to cut thin shavings by turning the wheel anti-clockwise. Tilt the plane to a different angle each time you make a stroke (Fig. 4).

▮ Small curves

Start with a flat-bladed **surform** tool (Fig. 5). Always work towards the end of the wood. Next use a file to remove any marks left by the surform. Finish with glasspaper wrapped round a block.

▮ Larger curves

Use a **spokeshave**, which leaves a good surface (Fig. 6). A round-bottomed spokeshave will be needed for shapes that dip sharply. Round surforms and files can also be used.

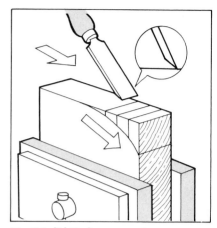

Fig. 1 **Thin timber and plywood:** use a coping saw.

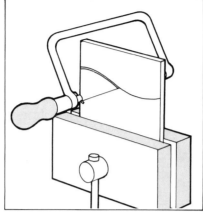

Fig. 2 **Solid timber:** use a tenon saw.

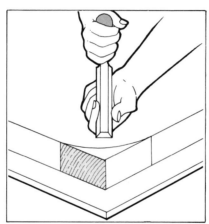

Fig. 3 **Rounding off sharp corners:** use a chisel, then a file or surform.

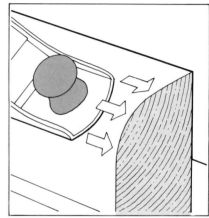

Fig. 4 **Rounding a long edge:** cut thin shavings

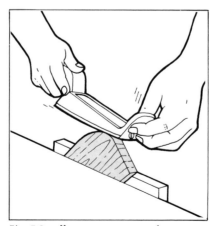

Fig. 5 **Small curves:** use a surform.

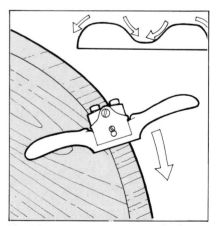

Fig. 6 **Larger curves:** use a spokeshave.

1 *Use step by step drawings to show how you would cut a flat boat shape from a piece of wood 15mm thick.*
2 *Draw a project that would need rounded corners to make it safer to use. A toy of some kind is one idea.*

Marking holes

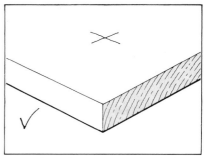

For accurate work you need to know *exactly* where to put the drill point.

Here's how to mark out holes on wood and metal.

If you don't make it too big the mark will disappear when the hole is drilled.

On acrylic use pencil or fine marker pen if the paper covering is off.

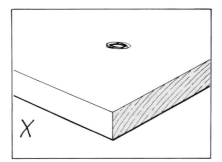

Fig. 1 The wrong way to mark a hole. A pencilled blob is not a good enough guide!

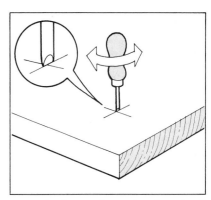

Fig. 2 The right way to mark a hole. A cross is much better than a blob.

Wood

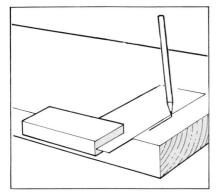

1 Mark the first line across the grain with a try-square and sharp pencil.

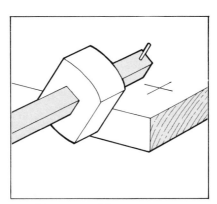

2 Use a **marking gauge** to complete the cross. Keep the same gauge setting if you want a row of holes.

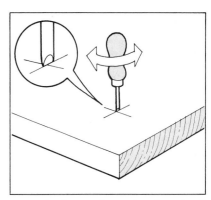

3 A hole made with a **bradawl** helps you to put the drill point in the right place. Put the bradawl down across the grain and twist it a few times.

Metal

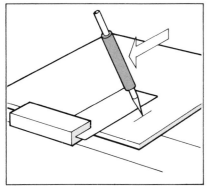

1 Mark the first line with an **engineers square** and a **scriber**.

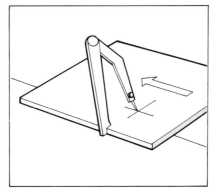

2 Use the **odd-leg calliper** to finish the cross.

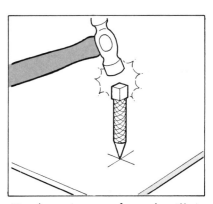

3 A **centre punch** mark will stop the drill point skidding across the metal.

When marking holes, why is a cross better than (a) a blob (b) a small dot?

The **wheelbrace** or **hand drill** and **twist drill bits** (Fig. 1) can be used for mosts materials. Tungsten-tipped bits are needed for drilling brick and concrete. Use a hand **countersink** to remove the rough **burr** on holes in metal. Carry the tool with its bit downwards to avoid accidents. *Turn the drill clockwise to make a hole.*

Changing the bit

Only use **bits** with smooth, round tops. Hold the **chuck** as shown in Fig. 2 and brace the tool against your body. With your free hand, open or close the **chuck** by turning the wheel. Your turning hand should also be used to put in or take out the drill bit.

Look into the empty chuck as you turn the wheel and you will see it working.

Holding the tool and the work

Keep your elbow tight against you to stop the tool wobbling. Turn the handle steadily.

Hold the work in the vice with some thick waste wood behind it. This helps you make a nice tidy hole and stops thin work bending or breaking.

Making small drill bits

Very small drill bits break easily. When drilling wood and soft materials it is better to make your own from nails or **panel pins.** Just cut off the head with pliers or **junior hacksaw** and file a chisel point on the sharp end.

Drilling to a certain depth

Stick a piece of coloured tape on the drill bit to tell you when you have gone deep enough (Fig. 5). This is useful when you want several holes of equal depth.

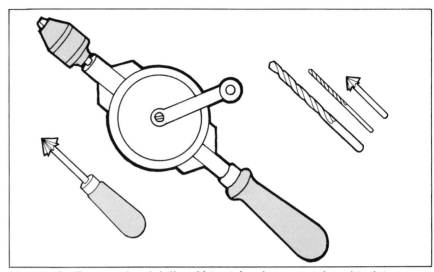

Fig. 1 A wheelbrace or hand drill and bits. A hand countersink tool (right).

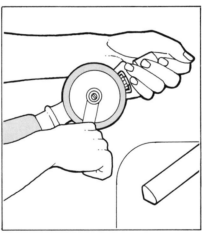

Fig. 2 **Changing the bit.**

Fig. 3 **Holding the tool and work.**

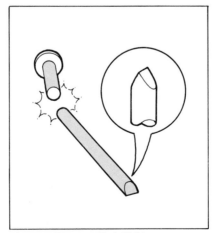

Fig. 4 **Making small drill bits.**

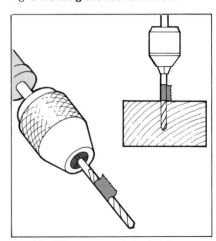

Fig. 5 **Drilling to a certain depth.**

Draw a set of pictures that show step by step how to drill a hole half way through a 20mm thick piece of wood.

Making larger holes in wood

Tools

The **carpenter's brace** (Fig. 1) is good for making large holes in wood. Only bits with 3-sides tops should be used (Fig. 1).

Some braces have a **ratchet** which lets you make holes close to a wall or other obstruction. You can find out about ratchets in Chapter 6, p. 108.

To change bits you hold the chuck still and turn the tool.

Don't make holes close to the end of wood or you may split it.

Holding the tool and work

To steady the tool, hold the non-turning hand tight against your hip (Fig. 2).

Boring straight through causes very ragged holes. Hold thick waste wood tightly behind the work or you will make a very ragged hole.

Preventing ragged holes — a second method

Work halfway through the wood from each side (Fig. 3). As soon as the point shows through, turn the work and bore from the other side. A friend can watch for the point to appear but be sure they are at a safe distance in case the bit bursts through accidentally.

Boring straight

Get a friend to tell you if you are keeping the tool level (Fig. 4).

Boring to a certain depth

The device in Fig. 5 clamps onto the bit to stop you boring deeper than you want. It is easy to make from two pieces of wood and two bolts. Coloured tape can be used to mark the bit instead.

> *Draw and label pictures of someone carrying a brace and bit (a) dangerously (b) safely.*

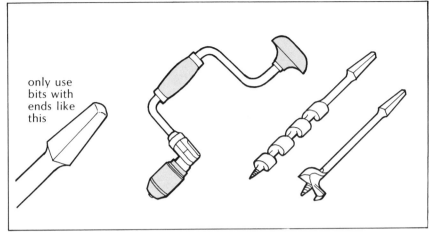

only use bits with ends like this

Fig. 1 **Tools:** a carpenter's brace and bits.

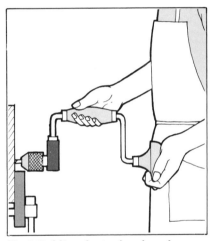

Fig. 2 **Holding the tool and work.**

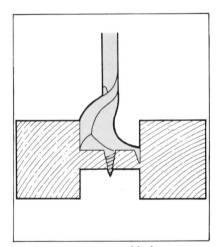

Fig. 3 **Preventing ragged holes.**

Fig. 4 **Boring straight:** ask a friend to make sure the tool is level.

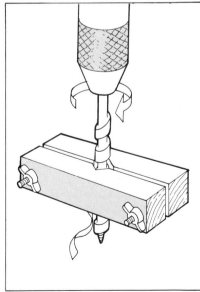

Fig. 5 **Boring to a certain depth:** this device is simple to make.

The drilling machine

The drilling machine saves time and effort, especially when drilling metal. It is the best way to make straight holes (at 90° to the surface) which is important on many projects.

▍Safety is important:

● Wear goggles.

● Tie back long hair and tuck your tie in.

● Know where STOP buttons are.

● Hold work properly (See Figs 2 and 3).

● Check with your teacher and follow any special instructions.

▍Changing the drill bit
This is like the electric drill at home. Raise the guard. Put the **chuck key** in the hole and turn it to loosen or tighten the chuck (see Fig. 1(b)). Use bits with *round* ends.

Never *leave the chuck key in. Replace the guard.*

▍Drilling holes to a certain depth
The rings on the side of the drill can be set to stop the bit going deeper than you want. One ring locks against the other to stop them working loose (Fig. 1).

▍Holding your work
Always hold thin pieces of metal in a hand vice (Fig. 2) Larger pieces must be held in a machine vice (Fig. 3).

This can also be used for small pieces of wood, larger pieces (of **wood only**) can be held in the hand. Hold all work **down** firmly, especially when the drill is nearly through. Take special care with acrylic which can crack or shatter. Have your holding method checked if in any doubt.

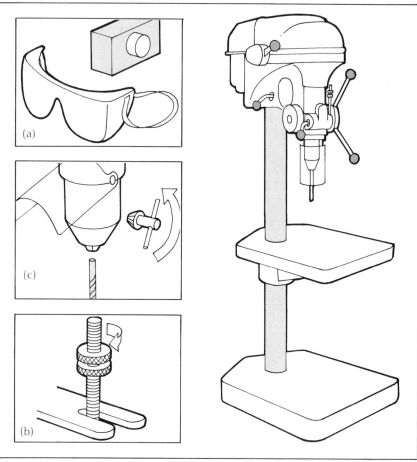

Fig. 1 A drilling machine (a) goggles and emergency stop button (b) changing a bit (c) drilling the hole to a certain depth.

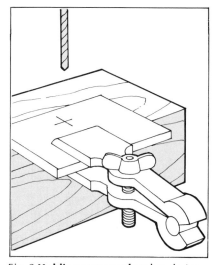

Fig. 2 **Holding your work:** a hand vice.

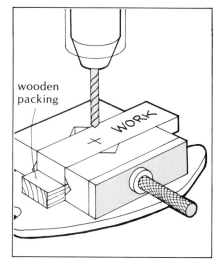

Fig. 3 **Holding your work:** a machine vice.

Design a poster to warn people against leaving the chuck key in when they switch on, and some other safety points.

Bending and forming wood

Curved shapes may be useful, like sledge runners, or mainly decorative, like bracelets. You could cut curves from a solid block but it can be quicker, stronger and less wasteful to **form** them by the methods shown here.

▌Forming plywood

Cut two pieces of solid wood or thick plywood to the shape of the curve wanted. Shape both pieces at once and check that they are 'square' Fig. 2(a).

The plywood has to be pinned and glued to the curves so that it overlaps a little (Fig. 2(b)). When the glue is dry it can be trimmed flush with the base with a plane. The grain must run *across* the curve.

▌Laminating veneers

Thin layers of wood called **veneer** are coated with glue and pressed into shape between shaped wooden **formers** (Fig. 3(a)). Wax the formers well or they may stick to your work!

When it is dry, remove the blank, laminated piece and trim or shape it (Fig. 3(b)). You could try using a bottle as a former for curves and circles. Hold the veneer on with strong rubber bands.

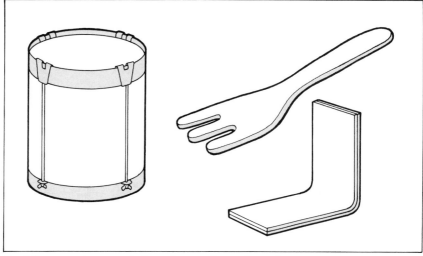

Fig. 1 Some projects made from bent or formed wood.

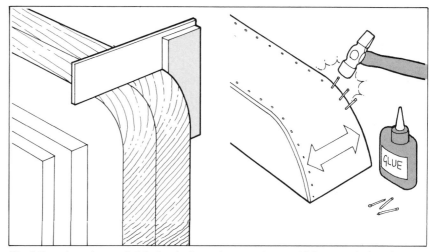

Fig. 2 **Forming plywood:** (a) check that edges are 'square' (b) pin and glue the edges.

1 Draw at least one project that includes (a) forming plywood (b) laminating.

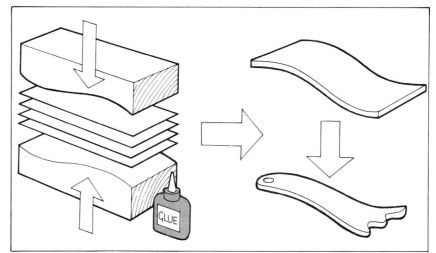

Fig. 3 **Laminating veneers:** (a) press glued layers between formers (b) trim the laminated blank.

Bending and twisting metal

You may want to bend metal to make decorative or useful parts for projects. Remember that once metal is bent you may find it difficult to straighten completely. Metal bent while cold becomes stiffer and more brittle where it is bent. This is called **work hardening.** Often you can just hold metal in the vice and bend it, but here are some special methods (Figs. 1-5):

Bending sheet metal
For 90° bends use **folding bars,** and a wooden block to protect the work (Fig. 1). Use a **hatchet stake** for sharper bends.

Bending several parts the same
This can be done using a jig (Fig. 2). The pegs can be moved for different bends.

Making the edge of thin sheet safer and stronger

1 Bend the edge to 90° using folding bars, then further with the **hatchet stake** (Fig. 1).

2 Flatten onto an old steel rule before beating to shape shown (Fig. 3). Take care not to flatten this **beaded** edge, which could be soldered (p. 92).

Bending heavier metal
For this you need to heat the work with a **brazing torch** (see p. 94). Wear a leather apron and take great care with hot metal. Hold the work in a vice (Fig. 4) while it is beaten.

Twisting metal
Twist wire by using a hook held in a hand drill. (Fig. 5(a)).

Square and flat strip is heated then held in a vice. Quickly twist it using a homemade wrench (Fig. 5(b)).

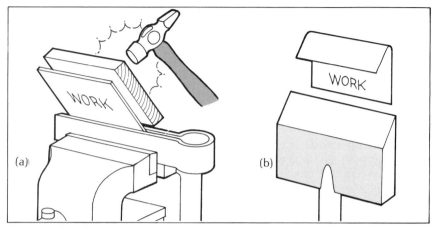

Fig. 1 **Bending sheet metal:** (a) using folding bars for 90° bends (b) using a hatchet stake for sharper bends.

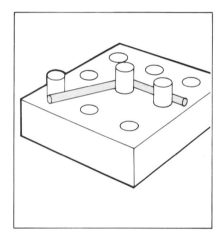

Fig. 2 **Bending several parts the same:** use a jig.

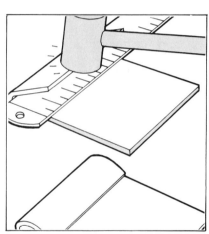

Fig. 3 **Making the edge safer:** make a beaded edge with a steel rule.

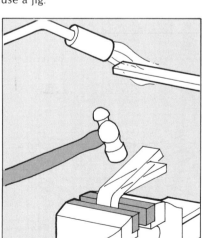

Fig. 4 **Bending heavier metal:** use a brazing torch.

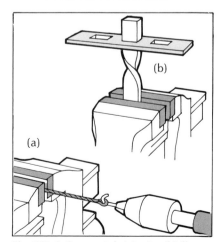

Fig. 5 **Twisting metal:** (a) wire (b) flat metal strip.

Draw at least one project made mainly by bending metal.

Bending and forming acrylic

Acrylic softens when heated gently. While hot it is easy to bend and mould. Take care not to damage it by overheating and don't touch the hot parts!

Bending acrylic
This is done on a strip heater.

1 Remove the protecting paper and mark the place to be bent with a felt pen.

2 Heat the bend line until the material gives easily when you try to bend it. Heat thicker material gently from both sides.

3 Bend to the angle you want and hold it there while the acrylic cools.

When you want a bend at a special angle a **former** is useful, especially if you want a number of pieces the same, as in Fig. 2.

Moulding 3D shapes

1 Soften the acrylic in a small oven.

2 Using gloves, drape the hot material over the one half of the former.

3 Quickly press the other part of the former into place and hold it while the acrylic cools (Fig. 3).

4 Trim to the shape you want (p. 68).

Blowing hemispheres
You need a special **former** and a pump for this (Fig. 4). Soften the acrylic in the oven and clamp it in the former. Pump in air and leave it there until the bubble is cool. Can you think of any uses?

Making raised patterns
Figure 5 shows how you can make raised patterns using metal shapes.

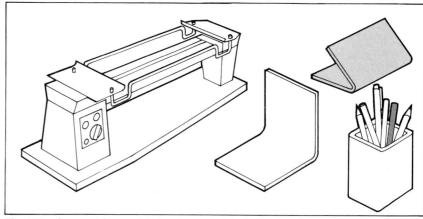

Fig. 1 **Bending acrylic:** a strip heater and objects bent on it.

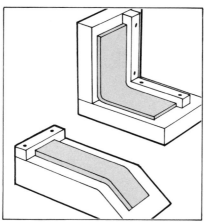

Fig. 2 **Bending acrylic:** using home made formers.

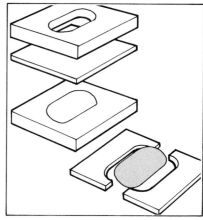

Fig. 3 **Moulding 3D shapes:** making a cockpit cover.

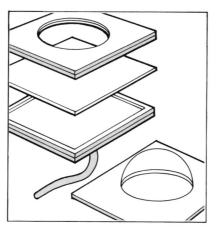

Fig. 4 **Blowing hemispheres:** using a special former and pump.

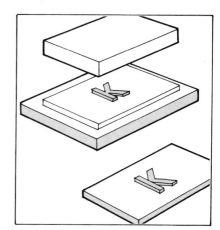

Fig. 5 Making raised patterns.

Draw some projects that could be made by bending acrylic. Modelling ideas by bending thin card will help you think of things. Acrylic is quite expensive so the projects should not be large.

Vacuum forming works by heating a sheet of plastic until it is soft then pulling it over a shaped former. When air is sucked out the plastic takes up the shape of the former.

Chocolate box trays, plastic egg boxes and many similar items are made in this way.

If your school has a vacuum forming machine, 3D signs, boat hulls and all sorts of complicated shapes can be made in seconds.

Formers
Formers can be made from things you find, or made from wood, plaster and other easy-to-work materials (Fig. 3). A former must not be sharp or it will puncture the softened plastic.

Also make sure you will be able to get your former out afterwards. Shapes that tuck under will become trapped by the plastic (Fig. 4).

How could you use the vacuum former to help people who are blind? Draw and explain at least one idea. Maps and signs may give you some ideas.

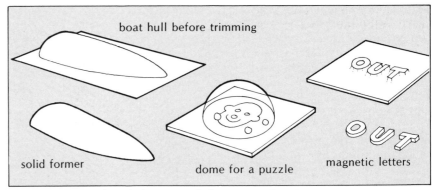

Fig. 1 Some examples of objects made by vacuum forming.

boat hull before trimming

solid former

dome for a puzzle

magnetic letters

Fig. 2 A vacuum forming machine in use.

Fig. 3 **Formers:** even modelling clay can be used.

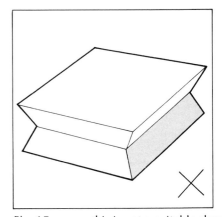

Fig. 4 **Formers:** this is *not* a suitable shape.

Questions

1 Safety depends on being careful and knowing what to do.

1.1 Look at the picture and make a list of the things that are wrong.

2 Red emergency STOP buttons switch off all the machines in the CDT room.

2.1 Make a plan of *your* room to show where the **STOP** buttons are.

2.2 How many can you remember without looking?

3 This wooden cow is part of a toy farm that your class is making for a local primary school.

3.1 Name and draw the tools you would use to mark out and cut the parts labelled.

3.2 How would you round off sharp edges and corners to make this safe and pleasant for children to handle? Use a drawing to help you explain.

3.3 You have been asked to make a whole herd of these cows. Draw and label the jigs you would make to save time and make all the cows the same.

3.4 A group of you is involved in making the herd of cows. Would it be better for each person to make their own cow — or would a production line be better with each person doing one stage then passing it onto another member of the team? Make a list of reasons for your answer.

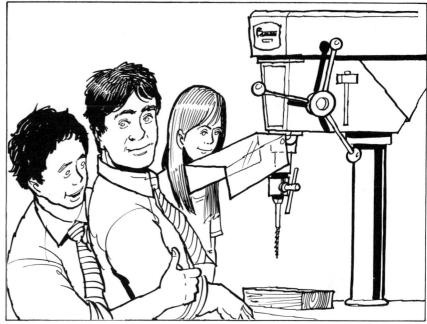

Question 1

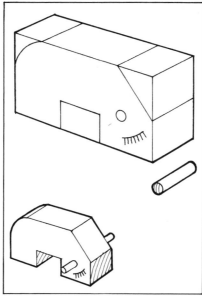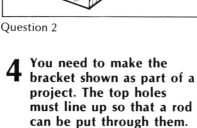

Question 2

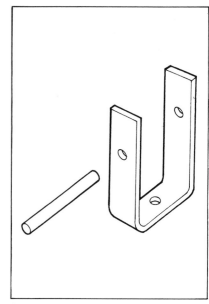

Question 3

4 You need to make the bracket shown as part of a project. The top holes must line up so that a rod can be put through them.

4.1 You are given a long length of *metal*. Use drawings to help you explain how you would:

(a) cut off a suitable piece;

(b) mark it out;

(c) make the bracket.

4.2 You are given a long strip of *acrylic* that your teacher has cut on the bandsaw. Explain how you would cut off your piece, mark out and make the bracket.

This book is 'sewn limp' — its pages are stitched together and glued to a 'limp' cover to make a book strong enough to cope with school use. This machine folds 3500 sheets of paper per hour.

Joining the parts of your project

Some objects can be made from one piece of material (Fig. 1(a)) but often you will need to join parts together (b). This chapter gives you joining methods to choose from when you are designing.

How to choose a method
When deciding how to join parts, think about these things:

● What methods can be used for that *material*, or mixture of materials?

● *How strong* does the join need to be?

● What *kinds of force* must it stand up to in use? (See Fig. 2.)

● Will the joint need to be *taken apart* sometimes?

● Will the joining method you choose *look alright* on your project?

Structures and forces
Objects that *support* something are sometimes known as **structures**. Here are some kinds of force that joints in a structure may need to resist.

● **Compression**, which is a squashing force (Fig. 2(a)).

● **Tension**, which tries to pull things apart (Fig. 2(b)).

● **Bending**, which stretches one side of the material and squashes the other (Fig. 2(c)).

● **Shearing**, which tries to slide one layer of a material over another parallel layer. Scissors apply a force like this (Fig. 2(d)).

● **Torsion**, which is a twisting or turning force (Fig. 2(e)).

Fig. 1 (a) some simple projects may be made from a single piece of material; (b) most projects will need several pieces which must be joined together.

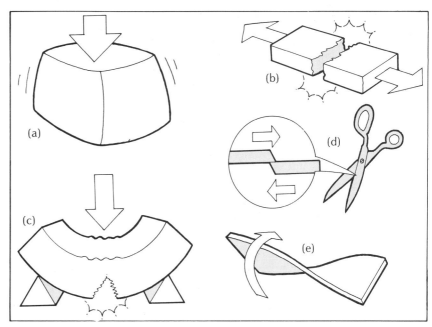

Fig. 2 **Structures and forces:** (a) compression (b) tension (c) bending (d) shearing (e) torsion.

1 *List objects made from one piece of material, then list objects made by joining pieces together. Which was the easiest to think of?*
2 *Look at Fig. 2(a)—(e). For each kind of force, give an example of an object or situation where it occurs.*
3 *Draw some other objects that support a load. Label parts with the kind of force they need to withstand.*

Which direction will the main force or load come from?

This can affect which way round you put a joint. Lots of joints are strong in one direction and rather weak in another (Fig. 1).

How strong does the project need to be?

This depends on how it will be used. A joint that is quite strong enough for one project might be too weak for another (Fig. 2). The pages which follow will help you to choose the right joint. Sometimes joining in an *extra* piece can make the project far stronger (Fig. 2(b)).

Will the joint need to be taken apart again?

You can probably think of things that need to be taken apart in use (Fig. 3). You might want to mend, clean or store them, or just replace batteries for instance. Some joining methods allow you to do this. Pages 90 and 91 show some methods.

Will the joint look right?

Some joining methods are chosen because they look attractive as well as being strong enough (Fig. 4(a)). Sometimes we want the joint to be almost invisible. On other projects the joint will not be seen, or the appearance is not important (Fig. 4(b)).

1 *Name some objects that are taken apart in use. Think about how they are joined. Draw at least one method if you can.*
2 *Name and draw at least one thing that would need a very neat or invisible join. Name at least one more in which the joint would have to be strong, but its looks would not be so important.*

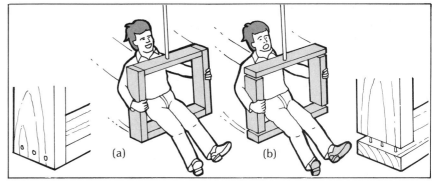

Fig. 1 **Which direction?:** (a) This joint is quite strong loaded this way. (b) It is much weaker loaded this way.

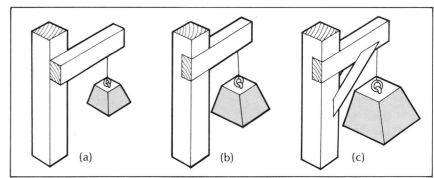

Fig. 2 **How strong?:** (a) This is suitable for light loads. (b) some joints are stronger than others. This is good for much heavier loads.

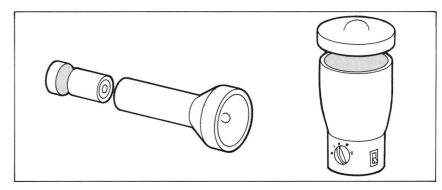

Fig. 3 **Will the joint need to be taken apart?:** This torch and liquidiser have joints that need to be taken apart.

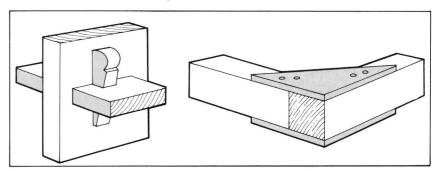

Fig. 4 **Will the joint look right?:** (a) This joint looks attractive. (b) This joint can be used when appearance is not important.

Joining materials with glue

Sticking parts together is an important part of making projects. The more the parts touch, the stronger the joint is likely to be.

Dust, grease, or varnish should be cleaned off as it can stop the glue making a good bond.

Glueing wood

Glueing the **end grain** of wood (Fig. 1a) makes a weak joint. The joint shape in Fig. 1b gives a larger glueing area and joins **side grain,** giving a far stronger joint.

Choosing the right glue is important. Here are some you are likely to need:

PVA (polyvinyl acetate)

This is a thick white glue used straight from the bottle (Fig. 3). It is very good for wood, card and similar materials. Use a waterproof kind if the work will ever get wet. The joint will be fairly strong after about twenty minutes.
Use a damp cloth to wipe off extra glue carefully before it dries, or a white mark may appear when you varnish your work.

Powdered resin glue

This is good for outdoor or floating projects and other work that will get wet.

Spoon out only as much as you need and add a *little* water at a time (Fig. 5). It is easy to add too much. Stir well; it should be a bit thicker than yoghurt.

It takes longer to set than PVA. Wash off any that gets on your hands and wipe any extra from the joint.

Show step-by-step how you would test the two joints in Fig. 1 to prove which was the strongest.

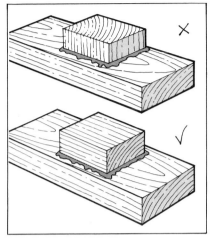

Fig. 1 **Glueing wood:** (a) glueing end grain is weak. (b) Glue side grain for a far stronger joint.

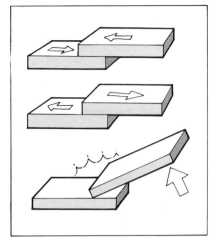

Fig. 2 **Glueing wood:** whether or not a glued joint will 'hold' depends partly on how the joint is loaded.

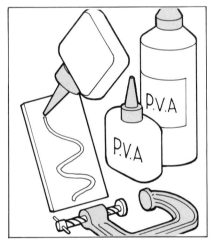

Fig. 3 **PVA:** this is easy to use straight from the bottle.

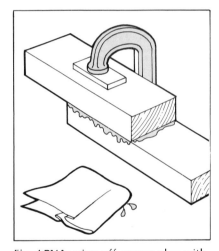

Fig. 4 **PVA:** wipe off excess glue with a damp cloth.

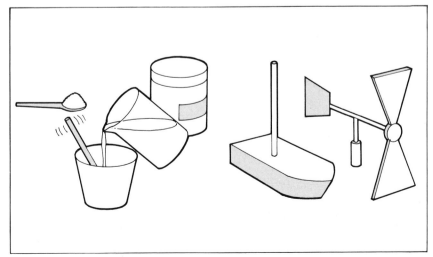

Fig. 5 **Powdered resin glue:** mix it with water. Use it on 'wet' or outdoor projects.

 # More glues to choose from

▌ Impact adhesive

This is brown and treacly with a strong smell. *Both pieces* have to be *thinly* coated and then left to dry before being pressed together (Fig. 1). It will join a range of materials but only makes a strong join when they touch over a reasonably large area. It is good for jobs that would be hard to cramp.

Some plastics are damaged by it, so test on a scrap piece. Keep it well away from flames and make sure the work area is well ventilated. It does *not* wash off your hands with soap.

▌ Epoxy resin

This is a *very* strong adhesive that will join most materials, such as wood to metal. One kind sets in about ten minutes. It is expensive, so use it only for small, special jobs. Mix a little from each tube together well, to start it setting (Fig. 2).

▌ Acrylic cement

This is a thin liquid which softens and welds acrylic pieces. Protect work with **masking tape** and paint the joint with a thin brush. (Fig. 3). Work away from any flame and have good ventilation. When making a 90° joint, use a simple jig.

▌ Hot glue gun

Hard **glue sticks** are heated in the gun and the hot glue is pressed out of the nozzle (Fig. 4). It can be used on a wide range of materials which can be stuck very quickly, but not as well as with epoxy resin. It is very good for small, fast repairs and fixing parts that would be hard to hold while normal glue sets. Do *not* use on long joints or it will set before you are ready. The nozzle and the glue can burn, so take care.

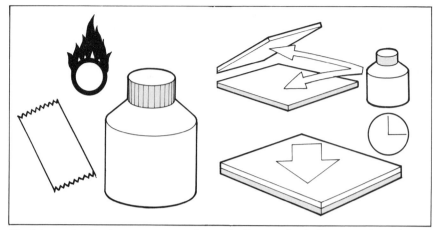

Fig. 1 **Impact adhesive:** use a spreader and allow to dry before pressing pieces together.

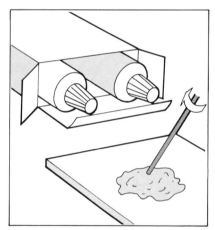

Fig. 2 **Epoxy resin:** mix adhesive and hardener.

Fig. 3 **Acrylic cement:** using a simple jig to make a joint.

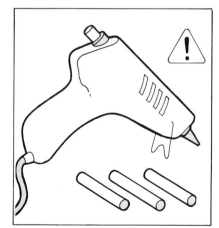

Fig. 4 **Hot glue gun:** allow a few minutes for the gun to warm up.

Fig. 5 **Hot glue gun:** press the stick gently to push out hot glue.

List pairs of material you might want to stick (e.g. wood to metal) and say which glue would be best.

Joining wood with nails and glue

Nailing and glueing is a quick way of joining wood (Fig. 1).

Types of nail

Panel pins are good for fixing box bottoms and neat, light jobs. The nail head can easily be punched below the surface of the wood using a nail punch to give a neat finish (Fig. 2(a)). The **oval brad** (Fig. 2(b)) comes in many sizes. Its shape helps to reduce the risk of splitting the wood and it is also easy to hide. **French wire nails** (Fig. 2(c)) are usually used on larger work when a neat appearance is not too important.

Blutack (Fig. 3) could be used to hold a pin while you get it started.

Dovetail nailing

Nails that slope as shown in Fig. 4 make a much stronger joint than nails that go straight in. Put the *middle* nail in first to stop the wood slipping. On narrow pieces, you may have to do without this middle nail.

Hiding nails

Use a **nail punch** (or **set**) of a suitable size to drive nail heads just below the surface (Fig. 5). Put **filler** in the holes to give a smooth finish.

Taking nails out

Use **pincers** with a **rolling** action to remove bent nails (Fig. 6). Holding your hammer well down its handle helps to prevent bending nails. You may have to punch a nail back through before you can grip it with pincers.

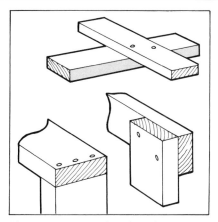

Fig. 1 Joining wood with nails.

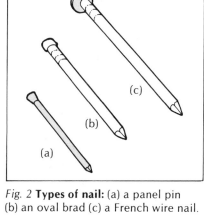

Fig. 2 **Types of nail:** (a) a panel pin (b) an oval brad (c) a French wire nail.

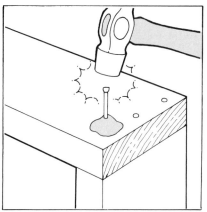

Fig. 3 Blutack is useful to hold a pin while you get started.

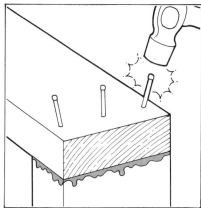

Fig. 4 **Dovetail nailing:** put in the middle nail first and remember the glue!

Fig. 5 **Hiding nails:** using a nail punch to drive heads below the surface.

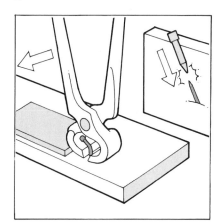

Fig. 6 **Taking nails out.**

1 *Draw and label some projects where French wire nails should be used.*
2 *Draw some more ideas (such as using Blutack) for holding small pins while you get them started.*

Putting screws in wood

Screwing is stronger than nailing if done properly and, unless glue is used, parts can be separated again without damage. Screws can be used to fix metal and other materials to wood (Fig. 1).

You will find you use **countersunk head** screws most. Here's how to fix them:

1 Mark holes on the thinner of the two pieces of wood. Do not place the screws in line as this weakens the wood (Fig. 2). Then use a drill that is the same size as the smooth part of the screw (or a little larger).

2 **Countersink** the hole so that the screw head will not stick out (Fig. 3).

3 Make smaller holes in the second piece. A **bradawl** is large enough for this, for most screws *you* will use (Fig. 4).

4 Use a long screwdriver that fits the screw slot well (Fig. 5). Too narrow a blade will make the screw hard to turn and damage the slot. Too wide a screwdriver may tear your work.

5 Avoid putting screws into end grain. They don't hold well and may split the wood unless a dowel is fitted (Fig. 6).

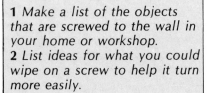
1 *Make a list of the objects that are screwed to the wall in your home or workshop.*
2 *List ideas for what you could wipe on a screw to help it turn more easily.*

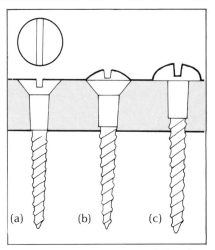

Fig. 1 Screws: (a) countersunk head (b) raised head (c) round head

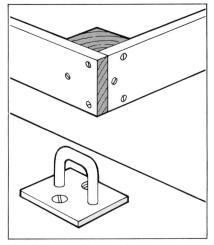

Fig. 2 Fixing with wood screws.

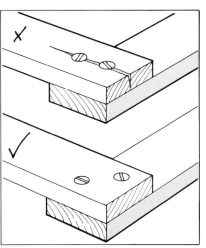

Fig. 3 Don't place the screws in line.

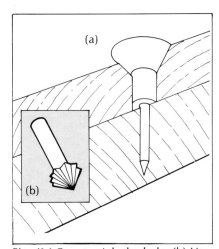

Fig. 4(a) Countersink the hole. (b) Use a bradawl to make a hole in the second piece.

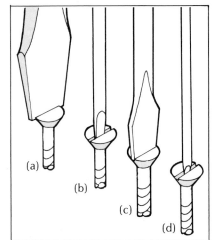

Fig. 5 Use the right size screwdriver: (c) is correct.

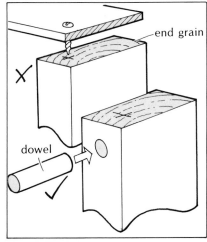

Fig. 6 Use a dowel rod if you have to put a screw in the end grain.

Joining metal with rivets

Rivetting is a way of joining metal or fixing materials like acrylic to metal.

▮ Types of rivet
There are three main types of rivet. Figure 1 shows how they hold pieces together.
(a) Snap head for a strong joint.
(b) Countersunk head for an almost invisible join.
(c) Flat head for thin material.

▮ Using snap heads
Drill all the holes needed in one piece but only one hole in the other (Fig. 2). One rivet is fixed first, then the missing holes are drilled using the first set as a guide. This makes sure that the holes line up.

One-and-a-half times the diameter of the rivet should stick through. Grip the waste part in a metal vice and cut it off with a hacksaw (p. 66) if you need to.

Support the rivet head in the hollow of a **'set and snap'** held in the metal vice (Fig. 3). Fit the hole in another 'set and snap' over the rivet and hammer once. This makes sure the pieces are tightly together.

Tighten the rivet as shown using the back of the hammer to gently shape a new head (Fig. 4). Mould the new head neatly using the hollow in a 'set and snap' (Fig. 5).

▮ Moveable joints
Use one rivet only. Put a piece of paper in between the pieces to be joined before rivetting (Fig. 6). Burn it out later using a brazing torch (p. 94).

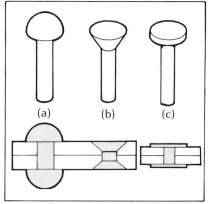

Fig. 1 **Types of rivet:** (a) snap head (b) countersunk head (c) flat head.

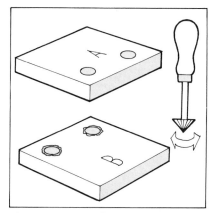

Fig. 2 **Using snap heads:** fix one rivet before drilling the other holes in B.

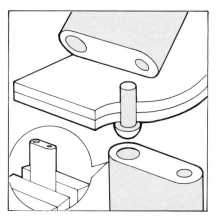

Fig. 3 **Using snap heads:** a 'set and snap' will make sure the pieces are together.

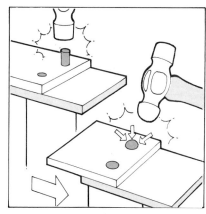

Fig. 4 **Using snap heads:** (a) tightening the rivet (b) shaping a new head.

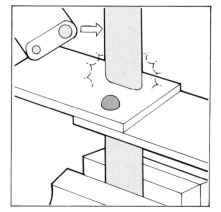

Fig. 5 **Using snap heads:** moulding a new head with the 'snap'.

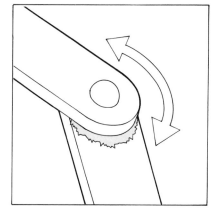

Fig. 6 **Moveable joints:** burn out the paper with a brazing torch.

1 *How much of a 3 mm diameter rivet should stick through the pieces before it is shaped into a new head?*
2 *Draw a project or part of one, where the moveable joint could be used.*

Joining thin materials quickly — pop rivetting

Pop rivets (Fig. 1) are a quick way of joining thin metal and other materials. Although not as strong as ordinary rivets (p. 88), pop rivets are much easier to use. They are especially useful when you can't get at both sides of the work to be joined (Fig. 2).

Drill holes in the same way as for ordinary rivets (p. 88).

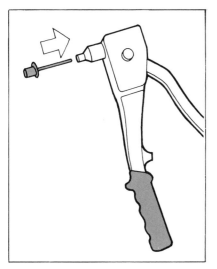

1 Load the pop rivet into the pop rivet gun.

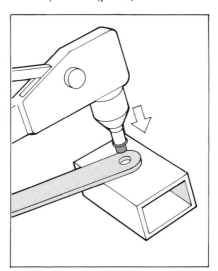

2 Once the rivet is loaded, put it through the hole in both bits of material.

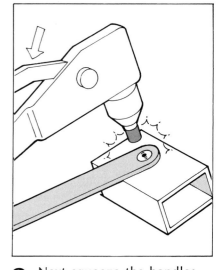

3 Next squeeze the handles until the rivet snaps off. You may need to grip further down the stem and squeeze again.
To finish, open the handles and drop out the waste piece.

Soft materials
Soft materials like rubber can be joined quickly with pop rivets. Use washers as shown in Fig. 1 to stop the rivet tearing through soft materials.

To make a moveable joint
To make a joint that will pivot and turn you should put some paper between the parts to be joined (as for normal rivets). This can be gently burnt out later on the brazing hearth (p. 94). Take care, because pop rivets melt easily.

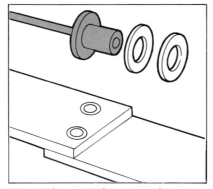

Fig. 1 **Soft materials:** use washers between the rivet and the material.

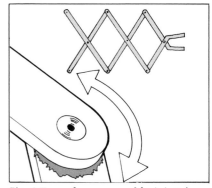

Fig. 2 **To make a moveable joint:** burn out the paper later.

1 *Say when a pop rivet is better than a normal rivet.*
2 *Say when a normal rivet is better than a pop rivet.*
3 *Every time a pop rivet is used the piece gripped by the tool is left over. Show as many uses as you can think of for these waste pieces.*
4 *Imagine that a younger or disabled person isn't quite strong enough to use a pop rivet gun in the normal way but they still want to do the job themselves. Use drawings to show how they could be helped to apply more force.*

Joints that can be undone

You may need to join parts that will need to be taken apart again later. For example, you may want to store, repair or adjust part of a project.

■ Different types of fixings

Nuts, bolts, self-tapping screws and **machine screws** are easy to salvage from broken household machines. As always, be sure it is *safe* and that you have *permission*.

Although mostly used for fixing metal parts, they can also be used on other materials. **Plain washers** stop the nut or bolt head from damaging the work. They are specially important when fixing things to wood and other soft or fragile materials.

Use **spanners** (Fig. 2) to tighten or loosen nuts and bolts. Always use the correct-sized spanner.

■ How to stop nuts working loose

Spring washers and **star washers** stop nuts working loose when a machine vibrates (Fig. 3). There are lots of these in washing machines.

Self-locking nuts have a plastic part which grips the bolt and stops them working loose (Fig. 4).

Using two nuts and tightening one against the other will stop them working loose. Special thin nuts can be used but normal ones will work.

■ Machine screws

Machine screws come with different heads (Fig. 5). Many are fixed with a screwdriver.

■ Self-tapping screws

Self-tapping screws are used to join thin metal (Fig. 6). They are hardened and when screwed into a suitable hole will cut their own thread.

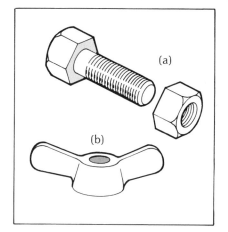

Fig. 1 (a) nut and bolt (b) wingnut: tightened with the fingers

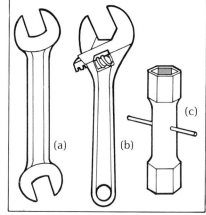

Fig. 2 (a) open ended spanner (b) adjustable spanner (c) box spanner

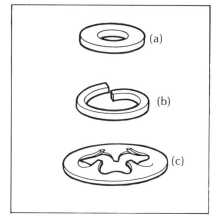

Fig. 3 (a) plain washer (b) spring washer (c) star washer.

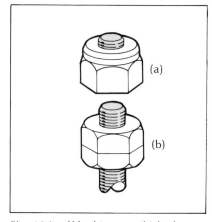

Fig. 4 (a) self-locking nut (b) lock nut. Both resist working loose.

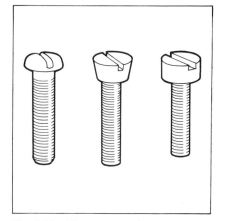

Fig. 5 **Machine screws:** these come with different heads.

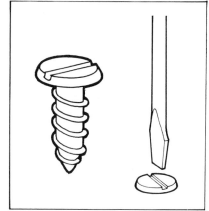

Fig. 6 **Self-tapping screws:** drill a hole first.

1 *Why are bolts often used to hold car and washing machine parts together?*

2 *List the machines in your house that you think include at least one nut and bolt.*

Joining metal — making screw threads

Screw threads allow you to fix metal (and some plastic) parts together so that you can take them apart easily when you need to. Nuts and bolts (p. 90) use threads. This page tells you how to cut your own threads in ordinary pieces of metal.

■ Male and female threads

You can make a *male* thread (like the thread on a bolt) and screw a matching nut onto it (Fig. 1(a)).

Or you might want to cut a *female* thread (like that in a nut) in a bar, and then screw a bolt into it (Fig. 1(b)).

When you need to make both parts yourself, cut the female thread first.

■ Making a female thread

1 First you mark and drill a hole. This must be a special size to match the tool that cuts the thread. This is called a **taper tap** and fits in a **tap wrench.** You may need a **second tap** and a **plug tap** too (Fig. 2). Your teacher will tell you the size.

2 Press the **tap** in the hole and turn it a little to get it started. Make sure it is *upright.* Add some oil. Turn the tap forward half a turn then back a quarter turn or it may jam (Fig. 3). Do this *gently* as smaller sizes of tap can snap.

■ Making a male thread

1 Hold the rod in a vice using emery cloth to protect it. **Taper** the end with a file (Fig. 4).

2 Fit the **die** into the **diestock** as shown (Fig. 5). Tighten the adjusting screw then the fixing screw.

3 Cut the thread by winding the tool back and forth (Fig. 6). Oil it to avoid jamming.

4 Try to screw the thread in. If it is too tight ask for help.

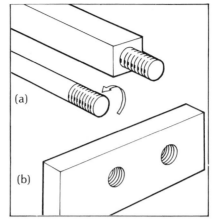

Fig. 1 (a) Male thread (b) female thread.

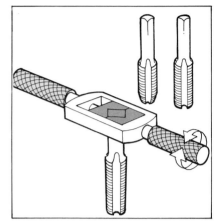

Fig. 2 (a) A taper tap in a tap wrench (b) second and plug taps.

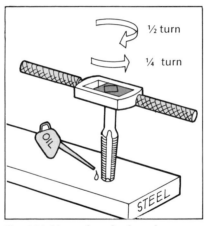

Fig. 3 **Making a female thread:** turn gently forward half a turn, then back a quarter turn.

Fig. 4 **Making a male thread:** taper the end of the rod by filing.

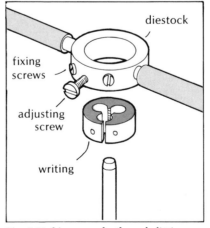

Fig. 5 **Making a male thread:** fitting the die into the diestock.

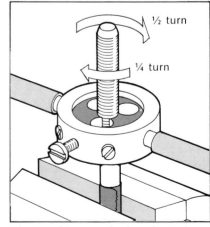

Fig. 6 **Making a male thread:** wind backwards every half turn.

List workshop and home equipment that uses at least one screw thread.

Joining metal — soft soldering

Metal pieces can be joined by soft **soldering.** A mixture of lead and tin, called **solder,** flows between the pieces and joins them as it cools. This is quite a quick method, but choose **brazing** (p. 94) where great strength or resistance to heat is needed in the finished project.

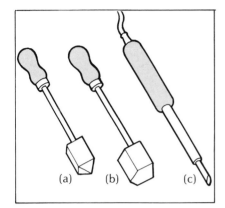

1 Decide which kind of soldering iron to use: (a) straight bit (b) hatchet bit (c) electric iron.

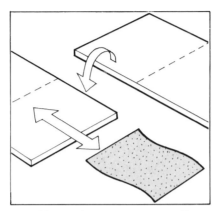

2 Clean the joint area well with emery cloth, then don't touch it.

3 Use a small brush to coat the joint with **flux** (zinc chloride) which keeps the joint clean. Flux is **corrosive,** so take care not to splash eyes or skin. Wash any splashes that do occur with lots of water and tell your teacher.

4 Heat the iron (non-electric ones only) until you see a *green* flame. Then stir it in a pot of flux and bits of solder. This is called **'tinning'.** Very dirty irons should be wire-brushed or rubbed clean with an old file first.

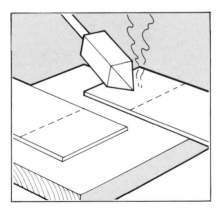

5 Heat the whole bit (not just the tip) then use it to collect solder. Both parts should be 'tinned' by wiping them with solder. Rest the work on a wood block which will not conduct away heat and cool it off too quickly.

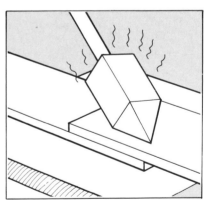

6 Brush the parts with flux again. Press them together; a wooden stick may help. Rub the hot iron slowly over the joint to re-melt the solder. This is called **sweating.** Wash the work to get rid of any flux.

> **1** What does 'corrosive' mean. Make up a symbol for it. Draw the standard symbol too if you can.
> **2** Why do you think soft soldered joints would be a bad idea if the project will get hot when used?

Twisting or taping wires together may be useful when trying out a battery-powered project but the joints can be unreliable. **Soldering** makes strong joints that conduct electricity well. Solder is melted between the parts to be joined by the heat from an electric soldering iron (Fig. 1).

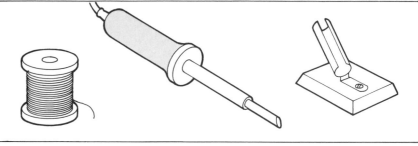

Fig. 1 A roll of solder, soldering iron and stand.

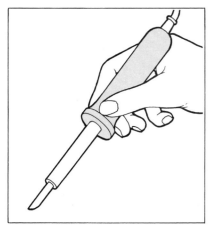

1 Hold the iron like a pen and take care to avoid burning yourself or the plastic sleeving on the wire.

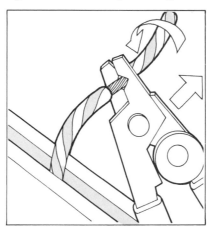

2 When using insulated wire you must remove some of the plastic insulation, or sleeving, with **wire strippers** before making a join. Set them so that they cut the insulation but not the wire inside. Grip the wire, twist the tool and pull.

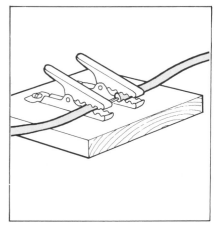

3 Use emery cloth or another abrasive to clean the parts to be joined. Then twist them together or hold with weights or clips.

4 Clean the hot bit on a damp sponge then melt some solder on the tip.

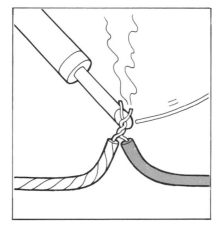

5 Hold the soldering iron on the joint which is stroked with special cored solder.

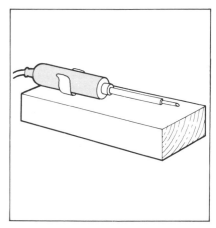

Sometimes it is easier to keep the tool still in a pipe clip and touch the work on it. Don't use too much heat or solder.

Joining metals strongly — brazing

Brazing is rather like soft soldering (p. 92) except that you have to make the work *much hotter* and the joint is *much stronger*. Steel parts are often joined in this way. **Brazing rod** is used instead of solder. Because you will use a **brazing torch** and the work will get very hot, *be very careful*. Always keep the torch pointing at the **hearth** and wear a **leather apron.** Check with your teacher if in any doubt.

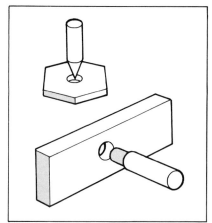

1 Parts of a project that might need to be brazed over the rod and bar. Clean the places that will join carefully, with emery cloth, then don't touch them.

2 Wipe flux paste on the joint to keep it clean while being heated.

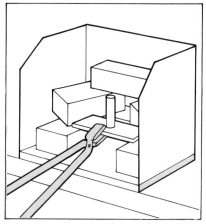

3 Put your work on the brazing hearth and arrange the bricks to reflect heat onto it. Laying the work flat on a brick will make it slow to heat up. Use tongs if the bricks are hot!

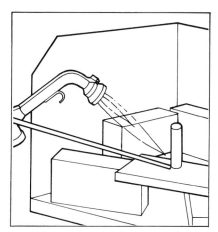

4 Keep the torch pointed at the hearth. Heat the work gently to dry the flux.

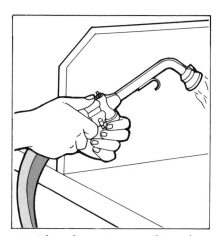

5 Then heat it more fiercely using the end of the flame. Touch the brazing rod on the joint. It will melt between the parts when the joint is hot enough.

6 Use tongs to cool the work in water. Clean it up with emery cloth.

1 *Say how brazing is like soft soldering (p. 92).*
2 *Say how brazing is different from soft soldering.*

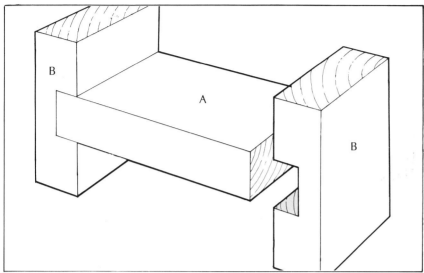

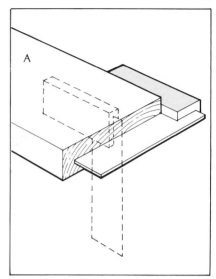

1 The **housing joint** is one way of joining wood in a T shape. It is often used to make shelves, tape racks and similar projects. You may have other uses for it. Like most joints in wood, it is much stronger in some directions than others. **Dovetail nailing** (p. 86) and glue are usually used to strengthen the joint.

2 The end of piece **A** must be straight and square. A piece sawn crooked will have to be planed in a special way (p. 69).

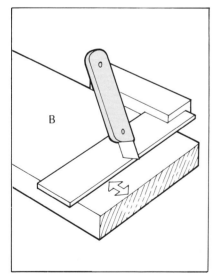

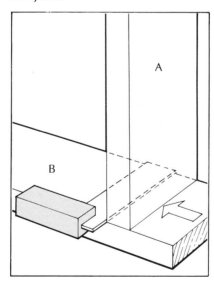

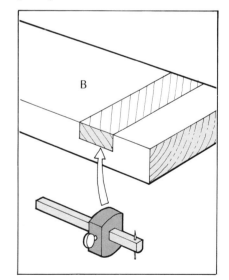

3 The first line on piece **B** is marked at least 25 mm from the end of the wood, or the piece on the joint may break. Narrow pieces can be marked two at a time.

4 Stand piece **A** against your try square and slide it along until it touches your first knife line. Squeeze the square against the wood, take piece **A** away and mark the second knife line.

5 Set your marking gauge to half the thickness of the wood. Use your gauge, square and knife to do the lines shown. These should be done on both edges. Shade waste as shown above.

1 Use the method shown on p. 29 to draw a housing joint.
2 Design projects that use at least one housing joint.

Cutting the housing joint

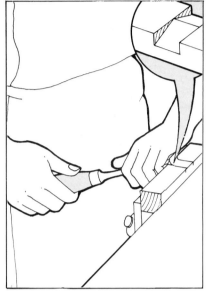

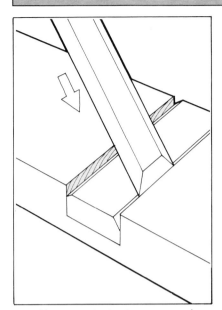

1 You must start your sawing in just the right place. Chiselling first, on the *waste* side of the knife line will help this.

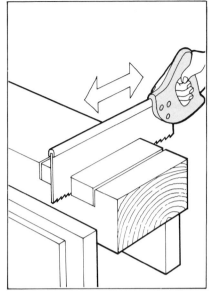

2 An extra saw cut will make chiselling the waste easier. Don't saw too deep.

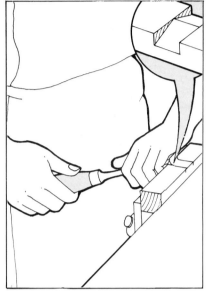

3 Rest your front hand on the vice and **chisel** a roof shape. Cut a little at a time. Turn the work to get at the other side.

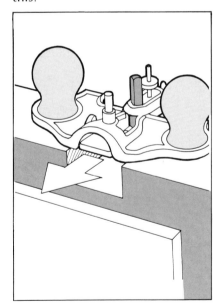

4 A **router** can be used to level your housing if you have one. Adjust it like this. Cut a little at a time and work to the middle from each side.

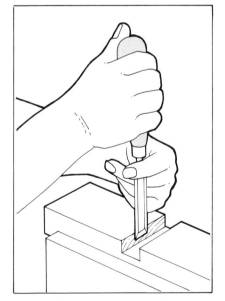

5 What if the joint is loose? (See page 97.) If the joint won't go together you can widen the housing a little by **'vertical paring'** as shown above.

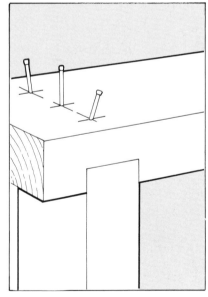

6 Hold the joint together with glue and dovetail nailing (p. 86). Wipe off excess glue. On narrow work, leave out the middle nail.

Page 61 gives a list of basic safety rules. Write down the ones that are most important when cutting a housing joint. What happens when someone ignores them?

The **lap joint** is neater and stronger than just nailing the pieces together for a wooden box corner (Fig. 1).

Method 1

1 Mark the waste on the sides only (Fig. 2).

2 Saw out waste wood and nail and glue the joint.

Method 2

1 Mark out and cut the joint like a housing joint that is 5mm too wide (p. 96). You can also adapt a housing joint that turns out too wide by accident (Fig. 3).

2 Push the joint tightly together and dovetail nail and glue as shown in Fig. 4. Ask a friend to help. On narrow work leave out the middle pin.

3 When the glue has set saw off most of the waste but leave some to be planed smooth (Fig. 5).

4 Pin and glue on the box bottom. This should overlap a little all round to be trimmed later. With the plane set to cut a little, hold the work in a vice and plane the edge like this (Fig. 6).

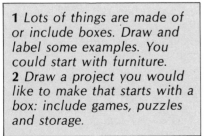

1 Lots of things are made of or include boxes. Draw and label some examples. You could start with furniture.
2 Draw a project you would like to make that starts with a box: include games, puzzles and storage.

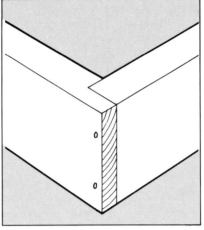

Fig. 1 A lap joint is neater and stronger than just nailing.

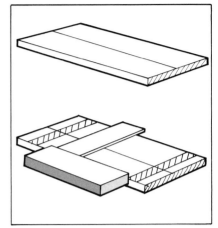

Fig. 2 **Method 1:** mark the waste wood like this. Do both box sides together.

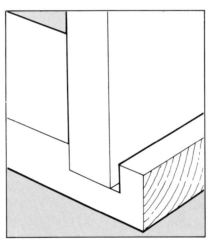

Fig. 3 **Method 2:** mark and cut out the joint like a housing joint that is 5mm too wide.

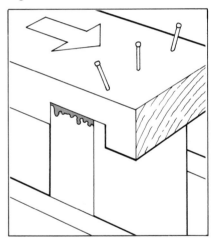

Fig. 4 **Method 2:** push the joint together, nail and glue.

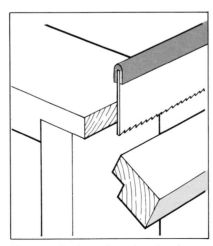

Fig. 5 **Method 2:** when the glue has set, saw off waste, leaving some for planing.

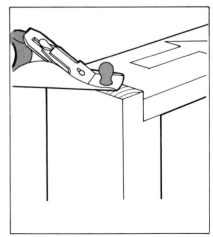

Fig. 6 **Method 2:** fix the box bottom. Hold the work low in the vice and plane a little at a time.

Joining wood in cross shapes, T shapes and L shapes

Halving joints are useful when you want to make **frames.** Lots of furniture designs are based on frames, such as dining chairs and benches. You can use frames as a base for vehicles, siege catapults, storage racks and many other projects.

▮ Types of halving joints

There are three types, **cross halving** (Fig. 1(a)), **corner halving** (Fig. 1(b)) and **T halving** (Fig. 1(c)). Can you work out how these joints get their name?

▮ The basic cut

Halving joints all have the same basic cut (Fig. 2). It is made with a router (supported by the shaded part in Fig. 2).

▮ Cross halving

1 Mark a line across both pieces (Fig. 3). Use a knife and squeeze the try-square against the wood. The position depends on where you want the joint.

2 Slide the try-square and wood up to the first line. Take the wood away and mark the second line with knife and try-square (Fig. 4). These lines *must* be the right distance apart.

3 Set your marking gauge to what looks like the middle of the thickness. When the point touches the same mark from each side, you have found the middle. Use the gauge, try-square and knife to mark the sides of the wood (Fig. 5). Do both pieces.

4 The waste part is shaded as shown in Fig. 6. Saw and chisel out the waste just like the housing on page 96. After chiselling, level off with the router if you have one.

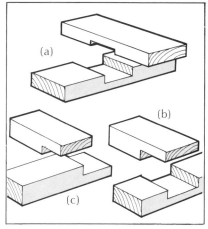

Fig. 1 **Types of halving joints:** (a) cross halving (b) T halving (c) corner halving.

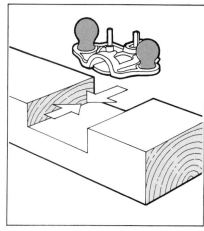

Fig. 2 **The basic cut:** the basic ingredient of halving joints.

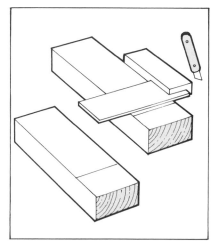

Fig. 3 **Cross halving 1:** mark knife lines where you want to start the joint.

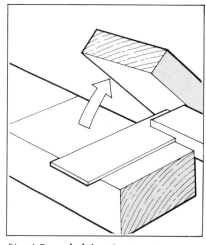

Fig. 4 **Cross halving 2:** use a try square to mark the second line.

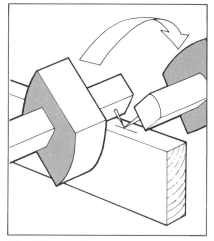

Fig. 5 **Cross halving 3:** use a marking gauge to find the middle.

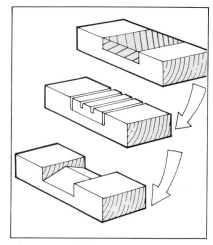

Fig. 6 **Cross halving 4:** saw and chisel out the waste.

T halving and corner halving

Page 99

▌ T halving

A T halving joint is like a cross halving joint with a piece cut off (Fig. 1).

1 Look at page 17 to find out how to mark and cut part A (Fig. 2). Use the other piece to help you. Saw just inside the lines for a snug fit.

2 Use a knife, try-square and marking gauge for this and shade waste as shown in Fig. 2.

3 Saw down. Take care to keep your tenon saw upright and stop at the line. Tilting the wood helps you to see the line better.

4 Glue and cramp gently (Fig. 3). Use waste wood to protect your work. When dry, hold it low in the vice and plane (Fig. 4).

▌ Corner halving

1 Mark and cut two pieces like part B of the T halving (Fig. 5).

2 Glue and cramp the joint. Use a try-square to check that it makes a right angle. Plane like this to avoid splitting (Fig. 6).

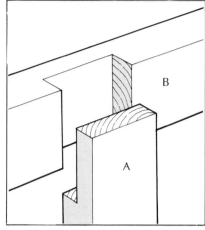

Fig. 1 **T halving:** a cross halving with a bit cut off.

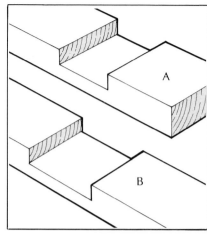

Fig. 2 **T halving:** one piece fits the other snugly. Cut **A** 5mm wider to allow for sawing off.

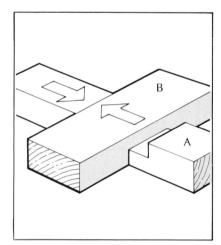

Fig. 3 **T halving:** push in the direction of the arrows as you tighten the cramp.

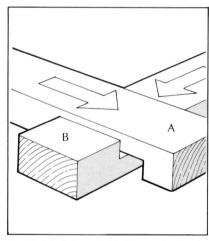

Fig. 4 **T halving:** hold the work low in the vice. Plane in the direction of the arrows to avoid splitting.

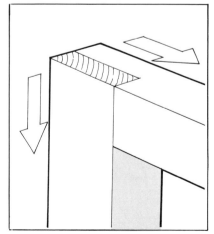

Fig. 5 **Corner halving:** push as shown while you glue and cramp the joint.

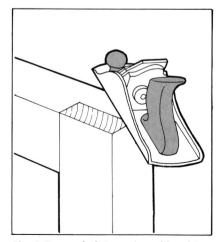

Fig. 6 **Corner halving:** plane like this to avoid splitting the end grain.

1 Draw some kind of seat or another project, that uses halving joints.
2 List and draw all the tools you would need to make a halving joint.

Questions

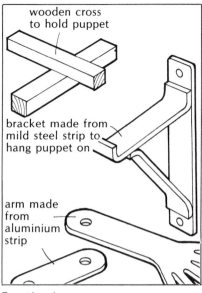

Question 1

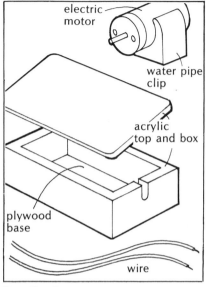

Question 2

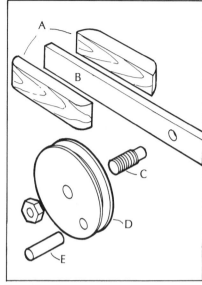

Question 3

Use drawings to help you answer these questions. Give *more than one* answer to each question when you can. When you suggest parts should be glued, say *which* adhesive you would use.

1 Here are three parts of a puppet project. The puppet will be hung from the wall bracket when not in use. This allows it to be seen and stops the strings getting tangled.

1.1 Show how you would join the bracket together. It is made from a mild steel strip.

1.2 Name the kind of force acting on part A.

1.3 The puppet is held by the wooden cross and its strings are fixed to it. Show at least *two* ways of joining the cross.

1.4 The puppet's arm is made from aluminium strip. Show how you would join the elbow so that it could move freely in the directions shown in the drawing.

2 This is a battery storage and control box for a motorised project.

2.1 Show how you would join the corners.

2.2 The bottom is made from plywood. Show how you would fix it to the box.

2.3 Show how you would fix the acrylic top on so that it could be taken off to change the battery.

2.4 Show how you would fix the switch to the acrylic top.

2.5 Show step-by-step how you would join the battery snap to longer wires.

3 Here is a line winder that could be part of a kite, harbour fishing or model boat project.

3.1 Show how you would join the wooden handles A to the metal part B.

3.2 Show how you would join the steel rod C to the main metal part B which is also steel.

3.3 What tool would you use to make the thread on the end of the metal rod?

3.4 The nut used to keep the plywood reel D on the metal rod, works loose when line is wound in. Show *two* ways of preventing this.

3.5 Name the glue you would use to fix the wooden handle E.

This is the machine on which this book was printed. The machine prints on two sides of a sheet of paper 1105 × 1650 mm at once and prints 3500 sheets per hour.

The way things move

Machines and mechanisms

Machines do work for us by converting energy from one form to another or passing it on.

Bicycles, egg whisks and hair driers are a few of the many machines in use everyday (Fig. 1). Even complicated machines are based on a number of simple **mechanisms.** You will learn about these mechanisms in this chapter. You will find out how to make actual mechanisms, to think about their importance in the world and how you can use them in your projects.

Input and output

Mechanisms are often used to change one kind of movement, **input,** into another, **output.** Knowing the basic kinds of movement will help you find out what is needed or describe what is going on.

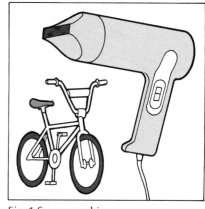

Fig. 1 Some machines.

Types of movement

1 Linear movement
Movement in a straight line. Sliding the bolt on a door is one example (Fig. 2).

2 Reciprocating movement
Movement backwards and forwards in a straight line. A handsaw moves in this way (Fig. 3).

3 Rotary movement
Circular movement like the wheels of a car or the turning of a windmill (Fig. 4).

4 Oscillating movement
Backwards and forwards following a curved path. Someone using a swing moves in this way (Fig. 5).

Fig. 2 **Linear movement.**

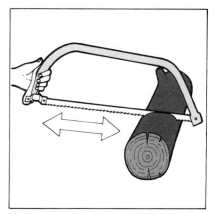

Fig. 3 **Reciprocating movement.**

Fig. 4 **Rotary movement.**

Fig. 5 **Oscillating movement.**

1 *What kinds of movement happen when these are used:*
(a) a hammer (b) a screwdriver (c) a breadknife
2 *List as many other examples as you can of the basic kinds of movement:*
(a) linear (b) reciprocating (c) rotary (d) oscillating
3 *Many pieces of playground equipment and funfair rides involve movement. Draw some and show the basic kinds of movement involved. Use arrows and labels.*

Levers and linkages

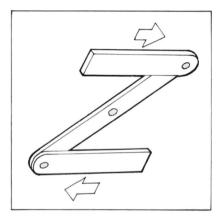

People have used **levers** since ancient times to increase the force they can put into a task, or to make a movement larger or smaller. There are three kinds or **classes** of lever. Figure 1 shows an example of each.

You can use levers to add movement to your projects. A **linkage** is a number of levers joined together. Use meccano or card strips fixed with paper fasteners to try out levers.

Fig. 1 Different kinds of lever

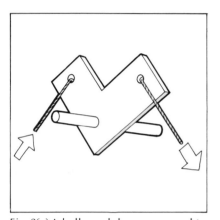

Fig. 2(a) A bell crank lever was used to ring bells.

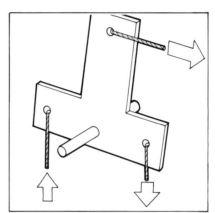

Fig. 2(b) Double bell crank lever.

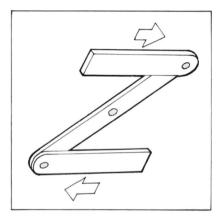

Fig. 2(c) This linkage turns a push into a pull.

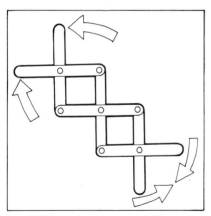

Fig. 2(d) **Lazy tongs** are sometimes used to pick objects from high shelves.

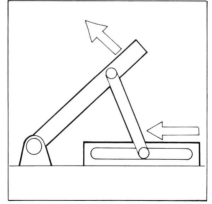

Fig. 2(e) This could tilt a drawing board or a hospital bed backrest.

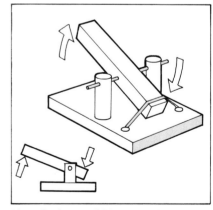

Fig. 2(f) This could be part of a model siege gun. It is a class one lever.

1 *List and sketch examples of levers in everyday use. Can you label them as first, second or third class levers?*
2 *Make card and paper fastener models of the levers and linkages shown on this page. Try altering the length of the levers and the position of the pivots.*
3 *Design a project or projects including levers or linkages.*

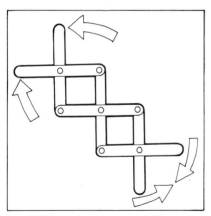

Page 103

Round-and-round and up-and-down — cams

Cams are a useful way of changing *round-and-round* movement, **rotary movement,** into *up-and-down* movement, **reciprocating movement.** Cams are an important part of machines that we need every day, including cars (Fig. 1). You can use them to make part of a project go up and down.

▌ How to make a cam

The best way to find out about cams is to make your own, like this:

1 Trace one of the cams at the bottom of this page (Fig. 5) onto corrugated cardboard. Cut it out carefully, trying to keep a nice, smooth shape.

2 Cut a strip of card to make the **follower**. Make a hole in this and the cam to take paper fasteners.

3 Fix your cam and follower together on a piece of corrugated card using the paper fasteners. Try different positions and make sure they move easily. You can turn the cam with a pencil point if you put in an extra hole.

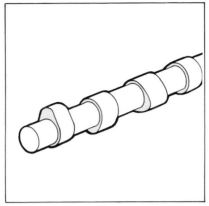

Fig. 1 Camshaft from a car engine.

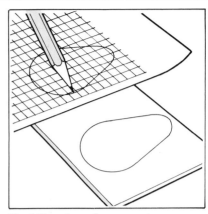

Fig. 2 **How to make a cam:** trace a cam (Fig. 5) onto corrugated cardboard. Cut it out.

Fig. 3 **How to make a cam:** cut a strip of card. Make a hole in this and the cam to take paper fasteners.

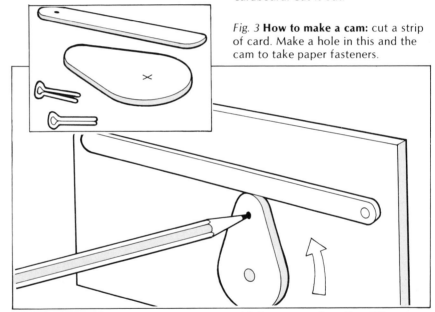

Fig. 4 **How to make a cam:** put your cam and follower together . Try different positions. Make sure they move easily. You can move the cam with a pencil point if you put in an extra hole.

1 *Make different shaped cams and try them with the follower. Try to guess how the follower will behave before you turn the cam. Make a drawing and notes to show what happens each time.*
2 *You could use a cam and follower to make a mechanical hammer. Draw a good shape for the cam based on your experiments in question 1.*
3 *Design a cam that will make the follower go up and down twice when the cam is turned once.*

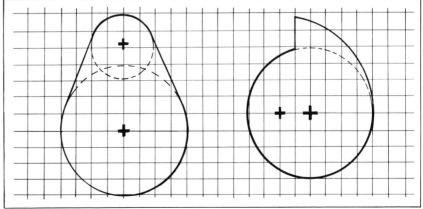

Fig. 5 Two cam designs to try out. Can you guess how the follower will move?

You can trace round a card cam to help you make a stronger one for use on a project. First try out the card one to make sure it gives the movement you want. Experimenting with card is quicker and cheaper than using harder materials.

When you have got the shape right, use it as a template (Fig. 6). Don't cut too close to the line as you will need to smooth the shape with other tools. Cut out your cam with a coping saw (Fig. 7).

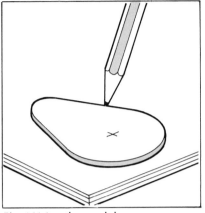

Fig. 6 Using the model cam as a template.

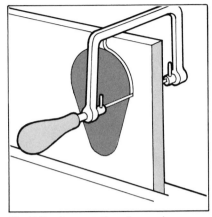

Fig. 7 Cutting out the plywood cam with a coping saw.

An example of the cam in use

Design problem: *Design and make a moving toy that a very young child can operate alone.*

The cam offers one way of solving the problem. A cam fixed to the axle of this truck (Fig. 8) makes the driver bob up and down. The faster the truck is pushed, the faster the man moves. As he is not fixed to the cam, the child can take him out to play with.

1 Name three tools that could be used to smooth a plywood cam after it has been cut out with a coping saw. (Fig. 7). Look in chapter 4 if you need help.
2 Draw a cam that would make the man in the truck (a) move a little (b) move a lot.
3 Design another pull-along toy using a cam to make something move.

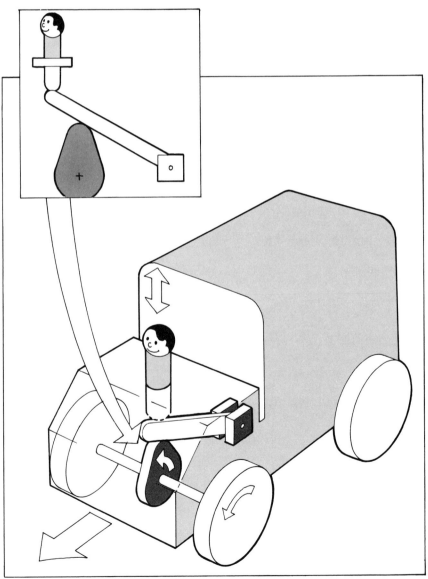

Fig. 8 A cam in use on a project — a push-along toy.

Pulleys

A **pulley** is a wheel with a groove round it's edge. You may have come across them in construction kits. Pulleys are often used to change the speed of a machine. The drilling machine in your CDT room uses them in this way. Washing machines, cranes, cars and many other machines include pulleys.

▌Using pulleys

Some ways of using pulleys are shown in Fig. 1.

Pulleys can be bought, salvaged or made. Scrapped cassette recorders are a good place to find small pulleys.

Construction kits are one of the easiest ways to find out what pulleys can do. Rubber bands can be used to connect pulleys. Card models are useful too (Fig. 2). They can help you to avoid costly mistakes with harder materials.

▌Making pulleys

You can make pulleys in plywood, using a hand drill held in the vice as kind of lathe (Fig. 3(a)). Get a friend to turn the drill handle while you cut the groove with a file.

Another way is to put a **bevel** (or slope) on two discs and then glue them together (Fig. 3(b)).

1 *Make a list of machines that use pulleys, using books to help you. This should help you realise how important pulleys are and will give you ideas about where to look for pulleys you could salvage.*
2 *Design a project that uses pulleys.*

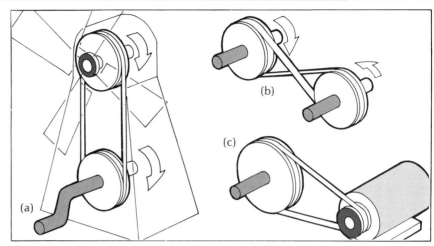

Fig. 1 **Using pulleys:** (a) transmitting motion — turning the handle at the bottom makes the windmill sails turn round (b) changing direction — by crossing over the rubber band between the pulleys (c) changing speed — slowing down by making the second pulley larger than the first.

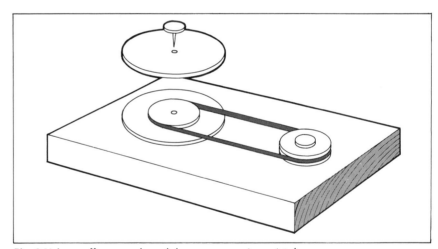

Fig. 2 **Using pulleys:** card models save expensive mistakes.

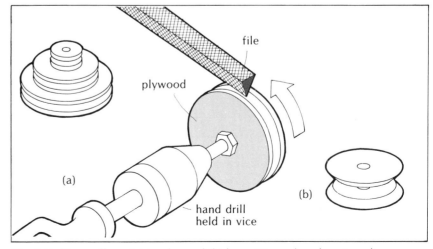

Fig. 3 **Making pulleys:** (a) in plywood (b) by putting a bevel on two discs

Gear wheels

A gear wheel has teeth round it's edge. These fit into other gear wheels with teeth the same size (Fig. 1). We say they **mesh**.

Changing speed

One use of gears is to *change the speed* of machines, or to increase the **turning power** or **torque.** Riding a bike with gears will give you some idea of how useful they are. Food mixers and cars are other machines that use gears.

Model gear wheels

You can make model gear wheels by sticking corrugated card round jar lids. Pin them to a base (Fig. 3).

Changing direction

Gears can change the *direction* and *angle* of a movement, say from horizontal to vertical (Fig. 4). These gears were made by glueing dowel rod into equally-spaced holes.

Rack and pinion

A **rack and pinion** (Fig. 5) is used to change round-and-round movement (**rotary movement**) into movement in a straight line (**linear movement**). When the gear wheel or **pinion,** turns, the rack moves in a straight line. What would happen to the pinion wheel if the rack was pushed?

This pinion was made by sanding one side of dowel rod until it was flat, cutting it into equal lengths and glueing some of them round a thick piece of rod, spacing them evenly. The rack was made by glueing the remaining pieces of dowel onto a strip of wood with spacing to match the pinion 'teeth'.

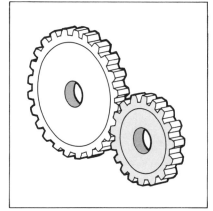

Fig. 1 Spur gears

Fig. 2 Construction kits are one way to learn about gears.

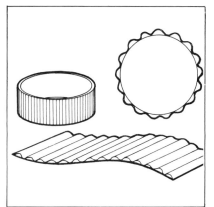

Fig. 3 **Model gear wheels:** use corrugated card and jar lids.

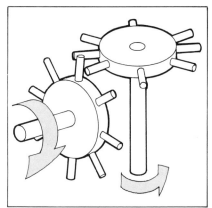

Fig. 4 **Changing direction:** from horizontal to vertical movement.

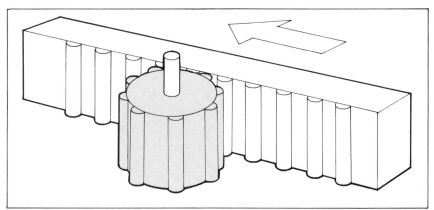

Fig. 5 **Rack and pinion:** these gears change rotary movement to linear movement.

1 *Give examples of machines that use gears in:*
(a) the home   (b) the workshop.
2 *Do you keep your eyes open? The drawing opposite shows some **bevel** gears. Which hand tool uses them?*
3 *Draw some ideas for using gears or a rack and pinion on projects.*

Bevel gears

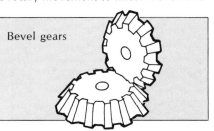

Making things turn one way only — the ratchet

A **ratchet** is a wheel with saw-shaped teeth round the edge. A tooth-shaped lever, called a **pawl,** allows the ratchet wheel to turn *one way only* (Fig. 1). When the pawl is moved out of the way, the wheel is free to turn either way.

Ratchets are found on winches, fishing reels and other devices (Fig. 2). You can use them too.

How to mark out ratchets

1 Keeping your compass point in one place, draw two circles. (The outer circle marks the top of the teeth. The inner circle marks the bottom of the teeth.)

2 Divide up the circle as shown (Fig. 3). This can be done with a protractor or a 30° set-square, T-square and board.

How many teeth would be marked out if you used the 45° set-square?

3 Draw in the teeth with a ruler.

4 You could now cut out the ratchet and paste it onto card if you wanted to make a model. Use thick card or thinner pieces glued together. A drawing pin or paper fastener will fix the ratchet to a base of wood or card. You could use plywood, aluminium or acrylic if the ratchet is to be used on an actual project.

Try pawls of different shapes. Stretch the elastic band by different amounts and make any other changes until your model works well.

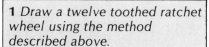
1 *Draw a twelve toothed ratchet wheel using the method described above.*
2 *Figure 4 shows one project using the pawl and ratchet. Design at least one more.*

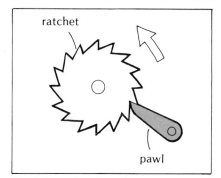
Fig. 1 A pawl and ratchet.

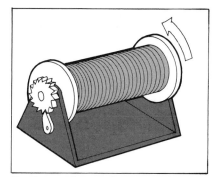
Fig. 2 A ratchet used on a winch.

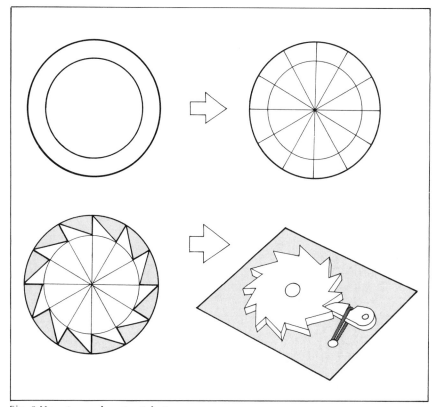
Fig. 3 **How to mark out ratchets.**

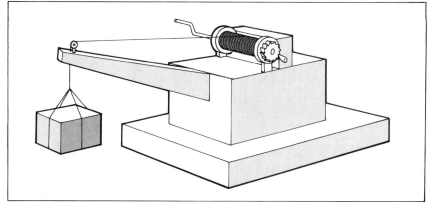
Fig. 4 The ratchet prevents loads being lowered accidentally.

Changing direction — steering

Almost all vehicles, from shopping trolleys to racing cars, need to be steered. Here are some ways of steering your projects. You can also get ideas by looking at wheelchairs, milkfloats, bulldozers and other vehicles.

Swinging beam steering

This is one of the simplest ways of steering something. It is used on road rollers, horse-drawn vehicles and home-made 'soap box' carts. It allows vehicles to turn tight corners; we say they have a **small turning circle.** Bad points are that the body shape has to allow plenty of room for the wheels to turn, and the vehicle would probably overturn if it cornered fast.

Castor steering

You have probably seen castors on furniture and shopping trolleys. They let the vehicle move freely in all directions. Castor steering is **self-centering.** This means that the vehicle will travel straight unless it is made to turn, by a push for example. You can salvage castors from old furniture or make your own. *The pivot must not be directly above the axle* (see Fig. 2).

Turning on the spot

The can-mobile in Fig. 3 is steered by switching on one motor, which operates one roller, to turn left, or the other to turn right. Bulldozers, army tanks and other tracked vehicles steer in a similar way.

Fig. 1 **Swinging beam steering:** very simple and good for turning tight corners.

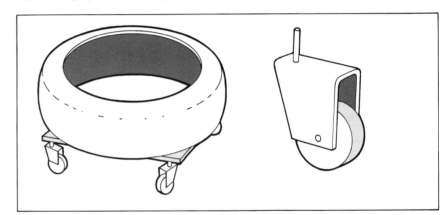

Fig. 2 **Castor steering:** lets an object move in any direction. Make sure the pivot is not directly above the axle.

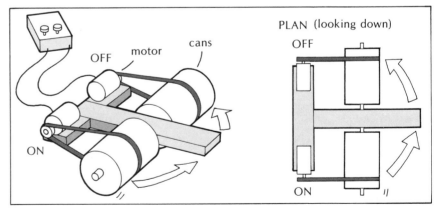

Fig. 3 **Turning on the spot:** switching motors on or off controls the steering

1 *Show how the rider could control the steering of the ride-on cart in Fig. 1. Show at least two ideas.*
2 *Show how you would make the castor riding platform (Fig. 2) better to use.*
3 *Draw a maze that you could make to test the steering of the can-mobile in Fig. 3.*

How to turn your project on and off — switches

Switches are important because they allow us to **control** all sorts of machines and electrical devices.

Think how many switches are used in your house every day.

A switch makes a gap in an electric circuit. When we want the current to flow we can close the gap using the switch. There are many kinds of switch to do different jobs (Fig. 1). You will probably recognise most of them.

Broken electric goods are a good source of free switches but you should *never* tamper with equipment without permission, and *never* when it is plugged in.

Push-to-make and push-to-break switches

These two useful switches may look the same but they work in opposite ways. *A push-to-make switch is only ON while it is pressed* (Fig. 2). *A push-to-break switch is only OFF when being pressed* (Fig. 3). Hidden under a money box, a push-to-break switch could set off an alarm when the box was lifted.

Paperclips and drawing pins can be used to make switches.

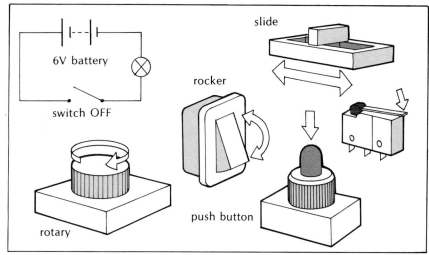

Fig. 1 Some of the kinds of switch you may find in your home

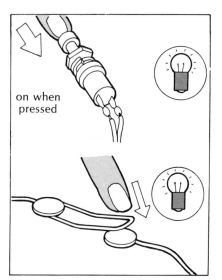

Fig. 2 **Push-to-make switch.**

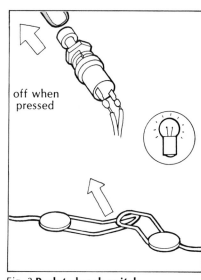

Fig. 3 **Push-to-break switch.**

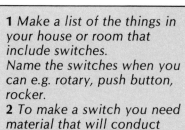

1 Make a list of the things in your house or room that include switches.
Name the switches when you can e.g. rotary, push button, rocker.
2 To make a switch you need material that will conduct electricity. List some of these materials.
3 The game shown in Fig. 4 is a kind of switch. Design a similar game or some other game based on a switch.

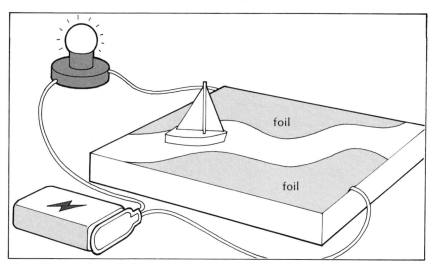

Fig. 4 The boat has a foil bottom. Careless navigating lights the bulb.

The pressure-sensitive membrane panel switch

Membrane panel switches are used on many modern devices that we see every day. Microwave ovens, cash registers and computers are examples. Compared with mechanical switches, they are cheap, reliable and easy to replace if damaged.

▌ How to make one

Here's how to make a simple membrane panel switch which need cost nothing and can be used on a variety of projects.

The list opposite tells you what you will need.

- Three postcards (or pieces of card).
- Some aluminium kitchen foil.
- Paste or glue stick.
- Craft knife, metal rule and cutting board
- Stapler
- Some insulated wire.

1 Mark out and cut a hole 25mm × 25mm in the centre of the middle card (Fig. 1). A smaller hole would make the switch less sensitive, a larger hole would make it easier to switch on. Don't make the hole too large or the switch may stay on!

2 Use the hole like a stencil to draw a square on the other two pieces. Don't cut them out this time (Fig. 2).

3 Cover the square on the top card with foil.

4 Stick two strips of foil across the square on the bottom card, leaving a gap between them (Fig. 3). Staple a wire onto each strip.

5 Tape the pieces of card together down one edge so that you can open the switch up if you need to make adjustments. The switch can now be connected to a circuit as shown (Fig. 4).

You can put all sorts of graphics on the top card or cut pictures from magazines. Cover with clear sticky plastic to keep the switch clean. Capacitors (p. 113) make the switch even more useful.

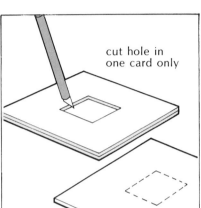

Fig. 1 Cut a hole 25mm × 25mm in one piece

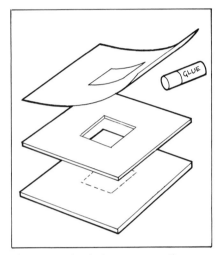

Fig. 2 Use the hole as a stencil.

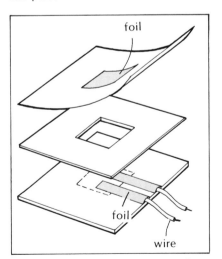

Fig. 3 Stick two strips of foil on the bottom card.

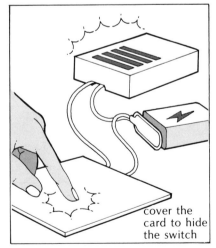

Fig. 4 Connect the switch to a circuit.

---

1 *Ordinary door-bell buttons are sometimes difficult for strangers to find, especially if their sight is poor. Design the graphics for an eyecatching membrane switch. This can be for your own room or some other situation of your choice.*
2 *Use drawings and notes to show how you would use a membrane panel switch to tell if someone was standing outside your door.*

The switch that works without being touched — the reed switch

The **reed switch** is switched ON when a magnet comes close to it. Just how close depends on the strength of the magnet and the way it is facing. Some kinds switch on only when a magnet is taken away (Fig. 1(a), 1(b)).

Switches of this kind are often used in alarm systems.

Reed switches are cheap and easy to use. With imagination they can be included in many different projects. Here is one idea to start you thinking.

A push-along toy

As the wheel goes round the magnet passes the reed switch and the light flashes on for a moment (Fig. 2).

This could be made into a push-along toy that a young child would enjoy.

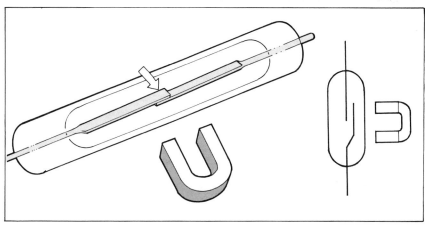

Fig. 1 (a) The reed switch (b) the symbol for the reed switch.

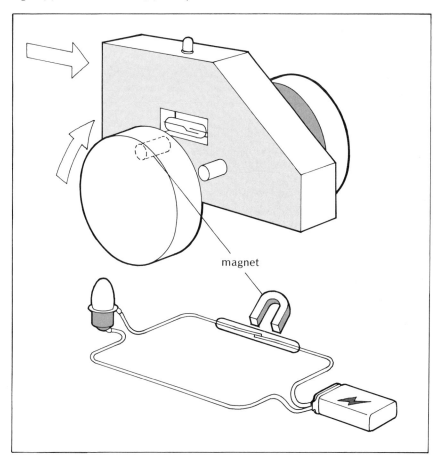

Fig. 2 **A push-along toy:** this project uses a reed switch. The circuit is also shown.

1 *What would happen to the light if the toy was pushed along slowly then more quickly?*
2 *Change the design of the body to make it more attractive and nicer to hold. You could sketch several versions. Move the light or add others if you wish. Remember that all toys must be safe.*
3 *How would you change this toy to suit a blind child? Explain with drawings and notes.*

How to keep your project working after it has been switched off — capacitors

A **capacitor** is an electronic part that can store electricity. Capacitors are used in radios, televisions, timers and many other electrical goods. You can use them to keep a buzzer or light on for some time after the project has been switched off, or even if the battery is taken away. This is good for alarms, toys and other projects.

The capacitors shown in Fig. 1 *must* be connected the right way round. You can buy capacitors or salvage them from broken electrical goods.

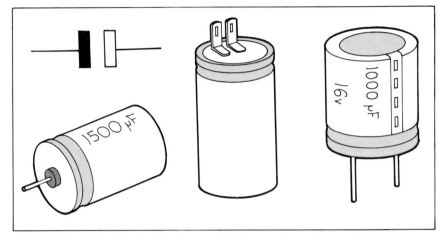

Fig. 1 Various types of electrolytic capacitor.

▌Capacitor project

The game in Fig. 2 and the circuit it contains, show a simple but interesting use of the capacitor. When a ball bounces off the character's mouth, a buzzer sounds for quite a long period. Although the membrane switch (p. 111) mouth is only switched on for an instant, that is enough to charge up the capacitor which then powers the buzzer. A larger capacitor would give a longer buzz. You could try capacitors with 1500 μF, 2200 μF, written on them. (μF means 'microFarad'.) Without the capacitor the buzzer would only sound for the instant that the ball hits the mouth. Be sure to use a miniature *piezoelectric* buzzer as this works best.

A light emitting diode (p. 114) or a small bulb could be used instead of a buzzer.

1 *Show some ideas for launching the ball at the character's mouth.*
2 *Design a game or alarm or some other project that uses this circuit. You may base your idea on the game shown if you wish.*

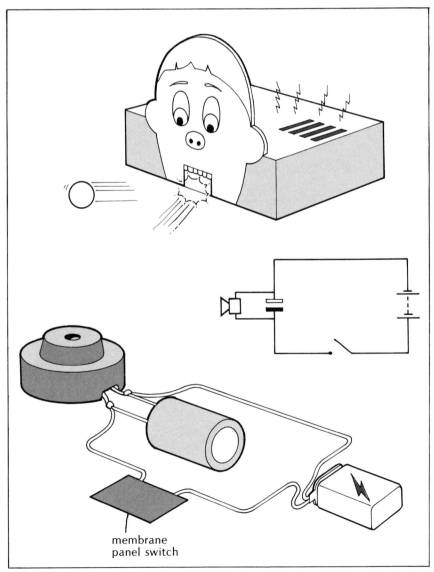

membrane panel switch

Fig. 2 **Capacitor project:** marble rolling game, circuit and circuit diagram.

The light emitting diode — LED

The light emitting diode (LED) is useful when a small coloured light is needed. Red, green and yellow LED's are available cheaply, you can even buy flashing LED's which contain microchips.

Using LED's

Many electronic devices use that LED's as **indicators,** to tell us the something is happening. Your stereo may have one to tell you that the power supply is on. LED's use much less electricity than light bulbs. This is important when a light has to be on all the time. Fire and burglar alarms often use LED's in this way to show that they are working.

How to connect a LED

Unlike a light bulb, the LED will only work if you connect + and − the right way round. You could join the parts with tape but **soldering** (p. 93) is far better.

1 The *short* leg must be connected to the *negative* side of the battery.

2 The *long* leg must be connected to the *positive* (+) side of the battery.

3 The **carbon resistor** can be connected to either leg. It stops too much electricity going to the LED and damaging it.

Design a device that would guide someone to a light switch or other object in a strange room in the dark. You should include an LED, an ON/OFF switch and a battery. Explain why an LED is better than a light bulb for this project.

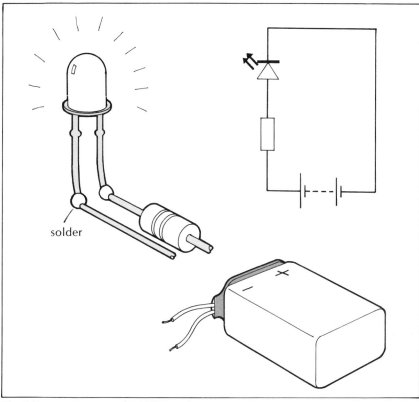

Fig. 1 How to connect the LED to a battery.

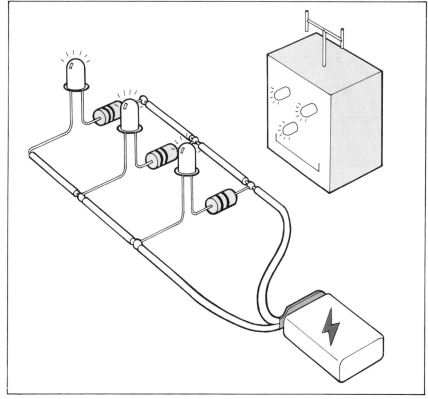

Fig. 2 How to wire up several LED'S.

Electric motors

Motors use electricity to make things move. Electric motors are very important to us; everything from robots to railways use them. Just think of all the motors that work for you each day.

Using motors on projects

You can use battery-powered motors on lots of projects. Unlike clockwork or twisted rubber bands, electric motors don't slow down unless you want them to or the battery runs out. Switches (p. 110) make them easy to control.

Most motors turn at high speed; pages 106 and 107 will give you ideas for slowing them down, if you need to.

Broken cassette recorders and battery operated toys have motors you can salvage and use (Figs. 1 and 4).

If you turn the wires to the battery round, the motor will turn the other way. A reversing switch (p. 116) is just an easier way of doing this on a project (Fig. 2).

Fixing motors

Your motor can't do much useful work unless it is held firmly. Some have fixing holes and are easy to screw or bolt in place but you may have to think of other methods. Water-pipe clips will fit some motors (Fig. 3).

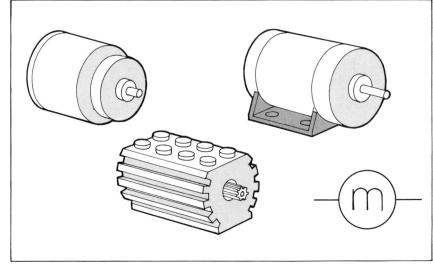

Fig. 1 You can use battery-powered electric motors on all sorts of projects.

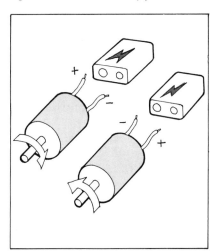

Fig. 2 **Using motors:** by swapping the wires, you can make a motor turn the other way.

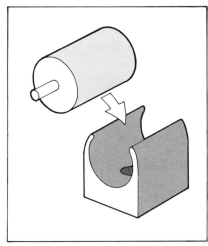

Fig. 3 **Fixing motors:** water-pipe clips will fit round some motors

1 *Make a list of the electric motors used in your house.*
2 *Imagine you have salvaged a motor from a broken toy. It is a smooth cylinder and won't fit into a pipe clip. Draw your ideas for fixing it to a project.*
3 *Make drawings of two projects that include a motor.*

Fig. 4 Motor and gearbox salvaged from a broken toy tractor

Making a motor turn one way, then the other — the slide switch

The **slide switch** can be used to make an electric motor turn one way and then the other. This could be useful on projects like winches, cranes and vehicles. Exchanging the wires on the battery would also work (p. 115) but using a slide switch is more convenient. These can be salvaged or bought.

Some slide switches have only two positions, forward and reverse. A more useful kind turns the motor OFF when it is set in the middle position (Fig. 1).

Fig. 2 shows how to connect the switch. You could twist the wires on and test it before soldering (p. 93) the joins.

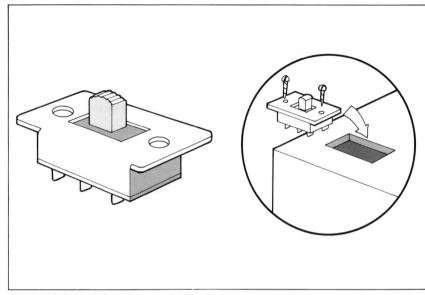

Fig. 1 A slide switch and how it is fixed

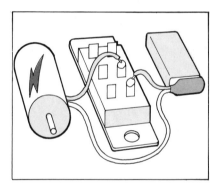

Fig. 3 Connecting the slide switch so that it just switches ON and OFF.

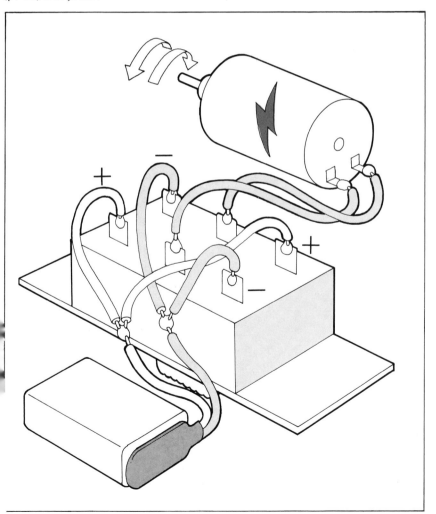

Fig. 2 Connect a slide switch like this to reverse your motor

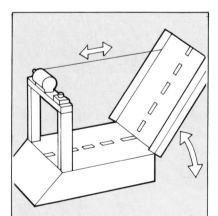

The lifting bridge is one idea for using the slide switch. Draw at least one other project when it would be useful to make a motor turn one way or the other.

Elastic bands for power

Elastic bands are usually used to hold things in bundles but *you* can use them to *store energy* and power your projects. They are cheap, easy to get and cost nothing to run. Bands are easy to use for fast movement that doesn't need to last very long, like a **catapult.** You may be able to think of ways to slow down the movement, making it last longer. Remember that elastic bands will need to be re-wound or re-stretched each time they are used.

When twisted to give rotary movement, (round and round), the speed is not constant, it becomes slower and slower.

▌ Using elastic bands
The drawings on this page give some ideas on how to use elastic bands in your projects.

In Fig. 1(a), the band is *stretched* and used as a catapult to launch a plane *in an arc*. In 1(b), the band is *twisted* and used to power the plane's propeller *round and round*.

In Fig. 2(a), the band is *twisted* to turn the can wheel *round and round*. In 2(b), a slice of candle slows down this movement.

In Fig. 3, the band is *stretched* to produce movement *in an arc*.

In Fig. 4, the band is *stretched* to produce movement in a *straight line*.

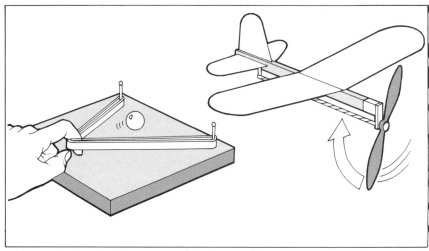

Fig. 1 **Using elastic bands:** (a) stretching to give fast movement in an arc (b) twisting to turn a propeller round and round.

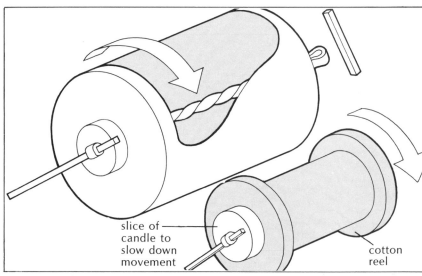

slice of candle to slow down movement

cotton reel

Fig. 2 **Using elastic bands:** (a) twisting to turn the can wheel round and round (b) slowing the movement using a piece of candle.

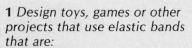

1 *Design toys, games or other projects that use elastic bands that are:*
(a) twisted
(b) stretched
The devices shown on this page may give you a few ideas.

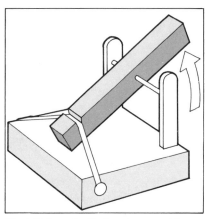

Fig. 3 **Using elastic bands:** stretching to give movement in an arc.

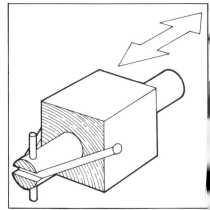

Fig. 4 **Using elastic bands:** stretching to give movement in a straight line.

Using fluids to power your projects — hydraulics

A **hydraulic** system uses *fluid* to transmit pressure and movement.

When a driver presses the brake pedal in a car, a hydraulic system makes the brake work. JCB's (Fig. 1) and many other heavy machines rely on hydraulics. Look for the pipes that carry the fluid.

The syringes in Fig. 2 are simple hydraulic systems. You can use them to work levers or move parts of your projects. Try different sizes of syringe to find out what they can do.

Using syringes
Here are some ideas to get you started:

1 Syringes can be used to push things at a distance, giving a kind of remote control (Fig. 3(a)). Thanks to the flexible tubing, your push can be aimed in any direction you want.

2 Using a three syringe system you can cause the same movement in two places at once (Fig. 3(b)).

3 Moving the little syringe a lot causes a small movement of the big syringe but the pressure is increased (Fig. 3(c)). Hydraulic jacks that lift cars work a bit like this.

Fig. 1 These 'caterpillar' bulldozers have hydraulic arms to operate the scoops.

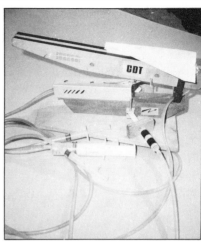

Fig. 2 Hydraulics are used on this paper plane launcher.

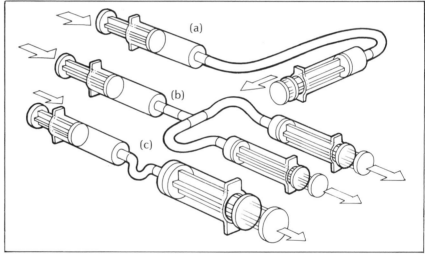

Fig. 3 **Using syringes** (a) flexible tubing gives remote control (b) a three syringe system causes movement in two places at once (c) different sized syringes control the amount of movement.

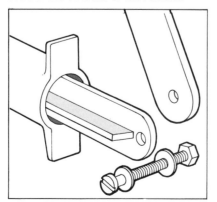

Fig. 4 A syringe is often more useful if it is connected to a lever. Shape the syringe carefully with junior hacksaw and fine file.

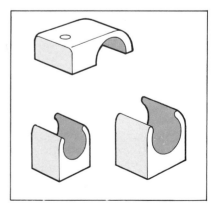

Fig. 5 Electric cable clips are good for holding small syringes. Small water pipe clips are good for larger syringes.

An elderly or disabled person cannot reach the items on a high shelf. Using simple hydraulics, design something to help them.

Air power — pneumatics

Pneumatics is about using *air* to move and control things. The robotic arms used in many factories are an example of pneumatics at work.

You can use simple pneumatics in your projects. Here are some ideas to get you started.

To make a basic power unit you need:

- An empty washing up liquid bottle
- A piece of plastic tubing that will fit tightly on the bottle top.
- A balloon (not the long kind).
- Some tape for joining the tube and balloon. Figure 1 shows how this is put together

When you squeeze the bottle in Fig. 1, air is forced into the balloon and it expands. Figures 2 and 3 give you two ideas on how to make the balloon do work.

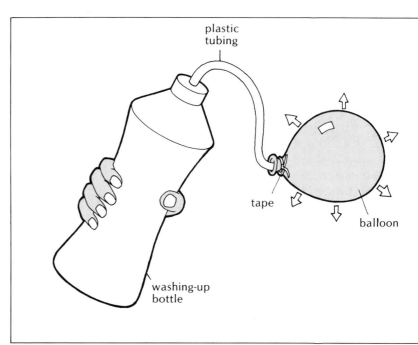

plastic tubing

tape

balloon

washing-up bottle

Fig. 1 **Pneumatics:** squeezing the bottle expands the balloon.

1 *Two ways of harnessing the balloon's movement are shown. Design projects based on each of these. A jack-in-the-box type toy is one idea, can you think of others?*
2 *One of the devices shown (Fig. 3) produces up-and-down movement. Show how you could change this to a different kind of movement*
3 *How you would find a leak in your pneumatic system? Use drawings to help you explain.*

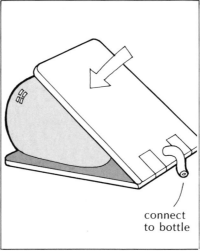

connect to bottle

Fig. 2 The expanding balloon raises the flap.

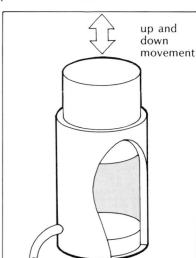

up and down movement

Fig. 3 The balloon expands and contracts to give up-and-down movement

Questions

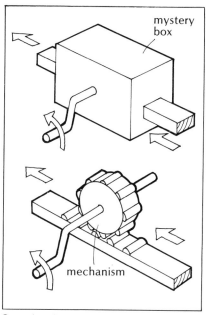

mystery box

mechanism

Question 1

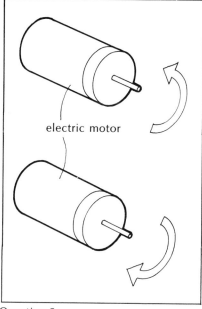

electric motor

Question 2

Question 3

All the information you need to answer these questions is in this chapter. Add some imagination and your own ideas. Most questions have more than one right answer!

1 **Here is a mystery black box. When the handle is turned *(input)* it causes a different kind of movement *(output)*. Next to the box its secret is revealed.**

1.1 Describe what kinds of movement are the input and output.

1.2 Name the mechanism that changes the movement from one kind to the other.

1.3 Draw your own mystery box. Label the input and output and say what kind of movement each is.

1.4 Use drawings to show how your box works. You may be able to show more than one way. If you have time, draw more boxes and explain how they work.

2 **You have been given an electric motor, a battery and some wire.**

2.1 Use step-by-step drawings to show how you would make the motor turn first in one direction and then the other.

2.2 Draw and name a more convenient way of making a motor turn in reverse. (You can use other materials than those above.) Say why this would be a better method to use on an actual project.

2.3 You need a switch that will make the motor stay **ON** or **OFF**. How would you make a simple switch to do this? Use drawings to help you explain. Show more than one idea if you can.

2.4 Most electric motors turn very quickly but you need to make part of a project turn slowly. Draw and label at least two ways of solving the problem.

3 **You have been asked to make a switch that will turn on when you press your toe down. It will be hidden in your shoe and could be used to turn on light-up disco jewellery or some other device of your choice.**

3.1 Use step-by-step drawings to show how you would make a badge that is comfortable — and works!

3.2 Draw what *you* would like to happen when the switch was pressed on.

3.3 Make a drawing of yourself to show where the switch, wires, battery and other parts would be.

3.4 Make a diagram of your circuit on its own. Draw wires shorter than they would really be or you might have to draw the other parts very small. Use the symbols for parts if you can.